Don't Eat The Soup As Hot As They Cook It!™

A WellChoices™ Solution

Don't Eat The Soup As Hot As They Cook It!™

The Story of a Family
Learning to Manage Stress Effectively
in Today's 24/7 World!

Cameron Johnston

Published by WellChoices™ Consulting Inc.
P.O. Box 2398, Station R
Kelowna, British Columbia, CANADA V1X 6A5

Phone: (250) 491 • 3495   Fax: (250) 491 • 3406
E-mail: cameronj@wellchoices.com   Net: http://www.wellchoices.com

National Library of Canada Cataloguing in Publication Data

Johnston, Cameron, 1949–

   Don't eat the soup as hot as they cook it

   ISBN: 0-9686504-1-4

   1. Stress management. I. Title.
BF575.S75J65 2001   155.9'042   C2001-910374-3

CREDITS
Copy-editing:
   Wayne Magnuson, Prairie House Books, Calgary, Alberta
Interior and Cover Design:
   Jeremy Drought, Last Impression Publishing Service, Calgary, Alberta
Original Cartoon Drawings:
   Nigel Druitt, Kamloops, British Columbia
Digital Enhancement of Cartoons:
   Virginia Boulay, V. Boulay Art & Design Ltd., Calgary, Alberta

Printed and bound in CANADA by Friesens, Altona, Manitoba

Dedication

To Fritz Wirtz Sr.

*A friend who inspired this book, the soup analogy,
and the outline for a stress management program
that has helped thousands of people.*

Contents

Acknowledgments

I'D like to say a heartfelt thank you to the following people:

To my wife, Shirley, who has been my partner in life for over twenty-five years and who endured, with honour, being my primary support during a very critical and stressful burnout experience. Her stress-coping skills have been well tested by her elementary school classes, by supporting me in a major transition to lifestyle consultant and professional speaker, and by raising our two beautiful daughters, Delight and Melanie.

To my parents, Bruce and Shirley Johnston, who have been lifelong supporters: dad, with his great capacity to enjoy people and life, and mom, with her deep spiritual and prayer experience.

To Dwight Rose, Bill Rochford, Brenda Cousineau, and Gordon Houston, for reading and editing early versions of the manuscript and for their valuable suggestions.

To Nigel Druitt for creating the original cartoons, and to Virginia Boulay for digital enhancement.

To Jeremy Drought for project management, interior design and cover design, and to Wayne Magnuson for copy-editing.

To the thousands of seminar participants who have benefited from the stress management material in this book. They come from a wide cross-section of nationalities and from all walks of life, including farmers, factory workers, homemakers, teachers, lawyers, social workers, nurses, physicians, researchers, pastors, law-enforcement officers, and business leaders. From teen to senior, their positive suggestions, ideas and stories have improved the presentation of our material and continue to be a key element in our success.

Preface

IT was about nine o'clock one evening when I visited Fritz Wirtz in his real estate office. We had been discussing an upcoming stress management seminar and as we were leaving, he said, "We hear a lot of talk today about managing stress. My father taught me a simple principle of stress management that has served me well over the years."

"What's that?" I asked casually.

"Don't eat the soup as hot as they cook it!" he replied.

He suddenly had my full attention but I hadn't quite caught the principle. "Pardon me?" I said.

"Don't eat the soup as hot as they cook it!" he repeated.

Sensing my interest and being willing to share the insight, my friend continued. "People can make your life very complex, if you let them. Strong reactions and high emotions in many circumstances can make life very challenging. Letting people and circumstances cool off can be very helpful.

"On the other hand," he proceeded, "people can deliberately arrange events to make a situation complex. The soup can get quite thick and hot. Let it cool off a bit before tackling a solution!" I was beginning to get it. *Don't eat the soup as hot as they cook it!* Here was a profound stress management insight.

If you were to meet my friend Fritz, you would get the impression that nothing bothers him. While very busy, he appears very relaxed and seems to have very little stress. The truth is, he has pressures and demands on his time and energy that few can appreciate. He has developed coping skills that allow him to manage his stress effectively. Not eating the soup as hot as they cook it is a principle he takes very seriously and applies to his everyday life. His spiritual experience and his deep faith in God are also major sources of strength and relaxation.

Recently, while greeting participants arriving at a stress management seminar, I just happened to pass by the registration table when a participant recognized Fritz and asked, "What are *you* doing here? You never have any stress."

After the woman had moved into the lecture hall, he whispered to me, "She thinks I have no stress. If she only knew!" He then shared with me just one major challenge that he was facing at the time. It was clear that he knew stress first-hand. Yet the appearance was that of a person who was relaxed and stress free. He had learned through years of practice not to eat the soup as hot as they cook it *and* how to cool it off.

There are a number of ways to cool the soup before eating it: let it sit awhile; stir in some crackers or cold milk; blow on it; drop in a couple of ice cubes; or begin by eating along the edge. Likewise, there are a number of ways to cool the stress soup in your life and reduce any negative effects. The intent of this book is to share with the reader a number of ways to cool your stress soup and, like my friend, be relaxed, confident and able to grow in our exciting world.

While most readers will need to cool off their soup, a few may need to heat theirs up. Boredom and/or living below one's potential can be as stressful as a super-busy lifestyle. In the following chapters we will explore the basics of managing today's stress to help both personality types.

As you follow the story of a contemporary family learning to deal with life and change, you will learn effective methods of enjoying and managing stress. Sit back, relax, learn, and enjoy.

Cameron Johnston
Kelowna, British Columbia
February 2001

The Modern Pressure Cooker

Introducing today's stress soup

BUSINESS was unbelievable for Bob Picco. His retail store was exceeding all projections and the future looked promising, yet Bob's personal life was spinning out of control. He was always busy but he found there was never enough time. He began to experience frequent headaches and chest pains. He became irritable with employees and family. His energy levels were low. Lack of sleep made him chronically tired, and mornings were becoming especially difficult for him to face.

"Wake up, wake up," Sue shouted as she shook her husband. Sue had begun noticing a gradual change in Bob and she was concerned. "Bob, start moving or you'll miss your appointment with the mayor!"

"Oh yes, the mayor!" With a groan, Bob realized that a new day was upon him. But where was his usual energy to attack it? Each day it seemed to take him longer and longer to get less done.

That morning, with no thought that his overwork and unbalanced lifestyle might be a contributing factor, Bob stumbled into the bathroom. Sue mumbled something about no hot water. He heard only, "Go easy on the hot water." Suddenly and without warning he was completely awake! The coldest water he had felt in years splashed over his tired body. His brain, now fully alert, recognized that to have a shower was to have it cold!

The water *was* cold but, to his pleasant surprise, it was not as cold as he expected. When finished, Bob was more awake than he had been in weeks. He was actually feeling good for the first time in months.

Bob related his surprise awakening to Sue over a quick coffee and cigarette, his usual breakfast.

"Oh," Sue responded, "that helps explain the article I read in the doctor's office the other day. It said a hot and cold shower is an excellent tonic. Not only will it wake you up, but alternating hot and cold is a type of vascular gymnastics that improves circulation and helps the body fight off disease. It actually increases the white blood count and improves the immune system."

Sue, now in her late thirties, was beginning to recognize her limited energy reserves. With a developing interest in health, she had been doing some extra reading on health issues and had recently registered for an upcoming wellness seminar. She hoped Bob would come along but thought it would be like pulling teeth and hadn't yet mentioned it to him.

"Wow!" Bob said as he rushed out the door. "You mean that was *good* for me? I *do* feel terrific. Maybe I'll try a cold shower again sometime!"

At about nine that evening, Bob was heading for the study as Sue returned from a parents' meeting.

"Bob, are you going to do work?"

"Yes, for a couple of hours."

"No, you are not!" Sue replied. "You are coming to bed with me. We need to talk!"

Bob had heard that authority in Sue's voice only a couple of times during their nearly twenty years of marriage. He knew it was the better part of wisdom to respond positively. Besides, he had no energy to protest. Work was over for today. The bed, he knew, would combine pleasure with a much needed reality check!

Tragedy On The Sales Team

Next morning, after a leisurely and nutritious breakfast, Bob Picco dragged himself into the study. He was exhausted and the day was just beginning. Sue's talk the night before was still challenging him. Her three ultimatums, which only a loving wife can give her husband, were still ringing in his ears!

Sue had made it clear that Bob must slow down and spend more time with her and the family. Secondly, he had to start taking better care of his health. Today he was to make a doctor's appointment for a complete physical. Finally, he must make some time to attend the upcoming wellness seminar with her.

Well, let's take these one at a time, Bob mused. *Slow down? That's impossible! Doctor's appointment? I don't have time. I am a bit tired, with an occasional chest pain, but at age 40 I'm in the prime of life! I'll take a short vacation in a few weeks and all will be fine. Wellness seminar? Have mercy!* he complained to himself. *Here Sue has definitely gone too far!*

As Bob developed his counterstrategy, the phone rang. It was his partner, Jim, and he was not his usual chipper self. "Bob, I've got bad news. Gary is dead. He keeled over this morning just after arriving at the office. A heart attack, it seems!"

Bob was speechless. His thirty-year-old sales manager dead of a heart attack! As reality settled in, Bob began to shake uncontrollably. Gary was the most talented salesperson on the team. Just yesterday, they were visiting with the mayor, planning a business trip to Asia. Now Gary was dead—at age 30!

The next few days were a blur, and shortly after the funeral Bob was in his doctor's office. As Dr. Moore examined him, Bob mentioned Gary's death. "Yes," the doctor said, "heart attacks are occurring at younger and younger ages and they are nearly all lifestyle related, and preventable. In fact," he continued, "with nearly half of all heart attacks, the very first symptom is that the person drops dead!" Then he leaned over and looked directly at Bob and said, "Bob, you are a prime candidate for a heart attack. You are a heavy smoker. You are significantly overweight and have high blood pressure. At your age and stress levels, eating the typical high-fat, low-fiber diet, combined with limited physical exercise, you are a heart attack looking for a place to happen. My advice is for you to make some serious lifestyle changes immediately. Most risk factors of heart disease can be reduced, and even if you have advanced heart disease, it *is* reversible. Stop smoking, slow down, and learn to manage your stress. Eat a more natural diet and begin exercising regularly."

Bob left the doctor's office in shock. *Maybe Sue was right*, he thought. *I need to make some significant changes. The question is how do you teach an old dog new lifestyle tricks? How does a person change long-established habits—especially on my schedule with all the time demands of running a modern business? Time is so limited and I'm too rushed.*

The C-Word Hits A Dear Friend

Sue Picco was delighted at the unusual willingness of her husband to agree to attend the wellness seminar. She was amazed at how fear can motivate, if only temporarily. Gary's sudden death and the doctor's serious chat, including his strange prescription, were not lost on Bob. He was actually eating a healthy breakfast and was trying seriously to cut back on his smoking.

The phone rang as Sue returned from taking the children to school. "Sweetheart," Bob said, "do you have some extra time today? Kathy is scheduled for major surgery first thing tomorrow morning. A biopsy confirmed fears of breast cancer and it looks serious. She's in the hospital now. Jim is with her but maybe a female friend would be helpful."

"I will *make* time." Sue answered in surprise.

"Good! See you at supper," Bob said as he hung up.

"Kathy with breast cancer! She's only thirty-five at the most—with a young family," Sue exclaimed aloud as she tried to deal with the terrible news. Jim, Kathy's husband, and Bob had been business partners for over ten years. She and Sue had also become good friends as their children grew up together.

Sue's visit with Kathy was more difficult than she expected. It was all so sudden and the doctor had just brought word that even with radical surgery, she had only six months to live. It was another case of late detection with seemingly very little hope.

Bob came home for supper exhausted. With two key men short in the office, he was stressed to the limit. So much for his stop-smoking and exercise plans. They would definitely have to wait. Over dinner, health issues dominated the discussion. All four teenage kids were full of questions. First it was Gary's sudden death and now Kathy's cancer. It was all so threatening. "Dad, are you going to die?" "Mom, are you going to get sick?" The questions were penetrating and frightening.

Sue finally admitted, "We really don't know the answers to all of your questions but we're definitely going to find some answers, and soon. It seems we're getting some strong signals that we can no longer take our health for granted."

The Wellness Seminar

"Welcome to *The Wellness Factor*, a unique seminar to help you take charge of your life. My name is Dr. Harvey Morgan. Our goals for this evening's session are to encourage you to take personal responsibility for your health and to help you find any areas where you need to modify your lifestyle for better performance."

Bob and Sue Picco were in the front row. It had been only two weeks since Gary's death and only a few days since Kathy's radical mastectomy. Bob and Sue's awareness of need and level of motivation were high.

"Relax!," the instructor continued. "We want you to enjoy our time together and begin to think through your current level of wellness. To begin, let me ask *what is wellness*? What do you think of when you hear the word *wellness*?"

"Energy," Bob said impulsively, totally forgetting the large number of people in the room. "Vitality," someone added. "Joy." "Contentment." "Endurance." "Sense of accomplishment." The answers came quickly from across the auditorium.

"Excellent," said Dr. Morgan. "Wellness includes much more than eating well and jogging three times a week. Greg Anderson defines wellness as 'Creating constant personal renewal, where we recognize and act on the truth that each day is a miraculous gift. Our job is to untie the ribbons and live life with joy.' The good news is that you can choose high-level wellness by taking personal responsibility."

Bob and Sue became so engrossed in the subject that they were surprised by the break. "Well," Bob said, as they left the lecture room for some fresh air and a smoke, "I knew health was important but I didn't realize that I had a choice in ensuring it. The thought of taking personal responsibility is frightening."

"For me," Sue interjected, "it's that heart disease and cancer—which account for nearly 75% of all deaths—are lifestyle related, and mostly preventable!"

"Let's not be late for the second half," Bob urged. "We don't want to miss anything." Sue was pleased that her husband was responding positively to a lecture on health.

The evening flew by. As they drove home, Bob's mind was racing. It was always racing. Those who knew him well would say that Bob was always running flat out. "Could Gary's death and Kathy's breast cancer have been prevented? Is there hope for Kathy?" Bob asked aloud, as if talking to himself.

"The presenter seemed to be saying a definite yes!" answered Sue. They both knew the time had come for them to act on a lifestyle change. The vital question now was *where to start*?

Don't Eat The Soup As Hot As They Cook It!

The weekend after the wellness seminar, Bob was reviewing the workbook materials. The personal wellness profile especially grabbed his attention. His score, in a range from excellent to poor, was poor—very poor. His list of personal recommendations was extensive, and included stopping smoking, beginning to exercise, reducing stress, reducing fat, and eating more fiber. With over twenty serious recommendations, Bob was motivated, scared, and almost over-whelmed. How could he put together a personal wellness plan incorporating all these new ideas? Change is common in business, but these were personal lifestyle changes!

Sue, whose wellness score was only marginally better, was a little ahead. She had already taken some planning steps and was just waiting for Bob to make a move. Bob finally spoke. "This all seems so overwhelming. I feel like we're living life totally backwards. I've smoked one to two packs of cigarettes a day for over twenty years. All the food I enjoy contains either too much fat or sugar—*empty calories*, they call it here. Jogging, I tried once and it bores me to tears. The choice seems to be, live a miserable life or enjoy it and die young."

"We definitely need to reprogram," responded Sue. "Are you ready?"

"I'm ready to start, but where?" Bob sounded thoughtful. "It seems to me we're looking at a long-term process. We need an effective plan that works but is also enjoyable."

"I've been studying the personal wellness action plan in our workbook," said Sue. "It seems like a place to start. Dr. Morgan really emphasized the importance of taking action immediately. I'd say now is the time to place a priority on the lifestyle issues we need to change, wouldn't you?"

"You've got that right," Bob replied. "But I think we need some group motivation—and more information. Did you pick up any of those flyers on upcoming seminars? I was particularly interested in the *soup* one, on managing stress. I could use some help with stress management!"

Sue looked quickly through the material and found the flyer. She read the title: *"Don't Eat The Soup As Hot As They Cook It!* Yes," she said, "this one does look interesting and I believe it covers a number of practical lifestyle habits that could be very helpful to us. The subtitle says, *A seminar that teaches you how to manage stress effectively in today's 24/7 World!* It begins in two weeks, on Tuesday nights at the Y, and runs for five weekly sessions. These topics sound very interesting," Sue went on: *"How Hot Is The Soup?, Let The Soup Sit, Thin The Soup, Stir The Soup, Play With The Soup, Make Sure The Soup Is Nutritious, Beware Of Poison In The Soup, Give Thanks For The Soup,* and *Eat The Soup Slowly And Enjoy It!* This sounds pretty good. Here's a session especially for you, Bob: *What If…You Already Ate The Soup Too Hot?* It identifies the stages of burnout in order to avoid or recover where necessary. The last session is just what we need. *Improving*

The Recipe For A Better Soup, which covers developing a personal action plan."

"I could definitely use the part on burnout," Bob said. "I can't seem to get my head above water lately. I may have already eaten the soup too hot!"

"The seminar seems to touch on exercise, nutrition, and a number of other things that would be very helpful to us," said Sue.

"Phone first thing Monday morning and sign me up," said Bob. "Stress management might be the place for me to start. Are you going to take the class on low-fat cooking? Maybe I should come with you, if men are allowed."

"Take it easy!" exclaimed Sue, quite impressed. Bob was taking this very seriously and she admired him for that. *When Bob decides, he acts*, she reminded herself. "Want me to come with you to the stress seminar?" she asked. "I could use a few stress management pointers myself."

"That would be great," Bob replied. "We're going to have to do it together to make this work! I'll also mention it to Jim and Kathy. They may be interested. Their stress levels have definitely been high lately."

All Stressed Out And The Day's Not Over!

"Mom, it's dad on the phone. He seems very upset." As Sue took the phone, she recognized Bob's excited voice. "I'm not going to make it home for dinner. You won't believe this day and, to top it off, a delivery truck just backed into my car. I'll fill you in on the way to the seminar. Bring me a sandwich and pick me up at the office. I'll eat on the road."

"Okay," was all Sue could muster. She was barely coping with her own day and she had completely forgotten about the stress seminar, which was to begin in two hours. The two weeks since they'd registered for the seminar had gone by in a flash, with no relief in their hectic schedules. Sue seriously considered cancelling but Bob was still determined to go, even with a day like this. This was a change! *Yes, we must go*, she decided. Jim had decided not to go as Kathy was not yet feeling up to it, but they had asked Bob and Sue to share the information with them.

Sue's day had begun with an emergency. Her dad had called just after breakfast. Her mom had fallen down the stairs and broken a leg. Other than being a bit shaken up, both were fine, but it took most of her morning. Arriving back from the hospital, she found the sewer had backed up, covering the basement floor with a foot of foul-smelling water. The plumber and cleanup crew had been working all afternoon.

Mid-afternoon, the school phoned. Their youngest daughter, Corina, was crying on the line. She had fallen during a gymnastic practice. The injury was not serious, but it meant she would miss the rest of the season, including the tour which she had been looking forward to for months. The grief caused by the loss of the trip was worse than the injury.

As a homemaker, Sue's days were usually full, but this was unreal! As she drove to collect Bob, she realized that she hadn't even had a chance to look at her *to-do* list for the day. *Yes, my to-do list! How could I manage without it?* she thought. *Even if I'm too busy to look at it.* She was in no mood to hear Bob's tales of woe but she had a good idea what was coming.

Bob had wound down somewhat by the time Sue picked him up. His day, hectic as ever, had a few additional challenges. Still without a sales manager and well into their busy season, today brought a serious threat of a lawsuit, and one of their best accounts had filed for bankruptcy protection while owing them a considerable sum. The car damage seemed only a minor annoyance.

Is this a night for a stress seminar? they were both wondering.

They arrived as the large hall was just filling. They had already paid. Why not stay for a while?

"We may not be able to stay the whole time," Sue heard herself saying to the lady at the registration desk. "It's been quite a day for both of us. We're stressed out," she added with emphasis.

"That's okay," the lady responded. "Relax! The evening won't be stressful. You'll enjoy the presentation. Here's your workbook, and there are still a couple of seats near the front." Sue consciously relaxed for the first time that day. It really felt good! *This may be helpful*, she thought.

As Bob and Sue Picco settled into their second row seats, they looked around and were impressed by the wide cross-section of people.

The age range was all the way from teenagers to seniors, with a large number of business and professional people present. They recognized a number of business associates and acquaintances.

"Welcome to *Don't Eat The Soup As Hot As They Cook It!* My name is Cindy Armstrong. I'll be your presenter for this seminar. Regardless of how hot your stress soup has been today, relax. We don't want this evening to be stressful. There's no final exam except for school teachers who insist that they need one!" A chuckle, mixed with a sense of relief, rippled across the room.

"I'm sure some of you have had a difficult day," she continued as she read from the screen. "Here are a couple of ways you can tell, early in the morning, if it's going to be a rotten day:

- **You turn on the news and they are showing emergency routes out of your city.**
- **You walk to work and find your dress is stuck to the back of your pantyhose.**
- **You call your answering service and they tell you it is none of your business.**
- **You put your bra on backwards and it fits better.**
- **Your wife says, "Good morning, Bill" and your name is George.**
- **Your car horn goes off accidentally and remains stuck as you follow a group of Hell's Angels on the freeway."**

The laughter was relaxing. Both Bob and Sue were caught off guard and enjoyed a much-needed belly laugh.

It Could Kill You!

After a short outline of the evening, the presenter moved right into her topic. "I have in my hand an interesting book called *The Joy of Stress* by Peter Hansen. Yes, you heard correctly. *The Joy of Stress!* Stress is not all bad. In fact, life would be very uninteresting without some stress. The only people experiencing no stress tonight are those in the cemetery!

"Stress is the spice of life. Problems come when our stress levels are more than our coping skills and reserves can handle. Few people have stress levels that are too high all the time, although it does happen to all of us from time to time. Our biggest challenge with stress is that most of us have not learned how to manage our regular stress effectively. Learning and developing these skills is what this seminar is all about."

Sue felt glad they had come. This would be good for both of them. She noticed Bob's interest, and truly began to relax. As the instructor directed them to turn to page one in their workbooks, Bob looked over and winked at Sue and whispered, "After today, I almost didn't come, but I'm glad we're here. We need this."

As the instructor continued, the video projector went dead. Everyone watched with interest as she handled the stress of the moment. Calmly she asked for an assistant to come and solve the problem. Someone asked, "Is this stressful?" It was obvious that she had dealt with this public stressor before and had developed the skills to deal with it effectively.

It took a few minutes to get the equipment up and running again. Meanwhile, Cindy continued. "What if you eat the stress soup too hot?" Then she answered her own question. "It could kill you! Eating the soup too hot accounts for over 70% of all visits to physicians and over 75% of all drug sales. Poorly managed stress in our society is a major contributor to heart disease, headaches, digestive problems, insomnia and a number of other serious, chronic ailments. Yes, being *hot* under the collar literally burns up your innards."

The projector returned to full power just as the instructor was encouraging participants to fill in the blanks in their workbook as they went along. "The answers will be on the screen," she said, and then asked, "What is stress? Stress is the body's response physically, mentally and emotionally to any demand made on it. This definition is adapted from Dr. Hans Selye, the famous stress researcher. Stress, in effect, is the wear and tear of life on the body, physically, mentally, and emotionally, caused by living. Our body's response to stress is often non-specific. That is, it can be very difficult to determine just how stress is affecting us. For instance, you may be having a number of physical or emotional symptoms, like chronic headaches, upset stomach, sleep difficulties, and boredom, so you go to the doctor. A number of tests are done and they find nothing physically wrong. The doctor then may ask if you are dealing with a lot of stress."

Bob whispered to Sue, "Maybe stress is the cause of my chronic tiredness over the last few months. After all, today's stress was not that unusual."

The instructor brought Bob and Sue back to the lecture when she said, "Now don't miss this. The amount of stress we experience is not so much determined by what happens to us as it is by the way we react to it. Suppose, for instance, that you had a car accident or an *almost* accident. The amount of stress you experienced would be in direct proportion to how you reacted. A relatively calm reaction will cause less stress than going over to the other driver and yelling at him for several minutes."

Bob poked Sue. "How did she know that a truck hit my car today?" and they both smiled. "My reaction to that crisis was mild compared to what it might have been," Bob whispered. That made him feel good.

"Stress," Cindy repeated for emphasis, "is not so much what happens to you as your reaction to it! This is very important. How much stress you experience from an incident or event, whether positive or negative, is determined by the intensity of your reaction to the event (the stressor).

"One evening, about two weeks ago," Cindy illustrated, "I was driving two hours west of here when a deer suddenly jumped out of the woods in front of me. Fortunately, I wasn't going very fast but just as I hit the brakes, my car struck the deer. It was a traumatic experience for me and especially for the deer. While the deer did not appear to be seriously hurt, it certainly had a few sore muscles. With no serious damage to my car, I travelled on, arrived safely and all was well. For me, a miss is as good as a mile and I went on my way, simply being more careful. My heart rate and blood pressure went up significantly for a little while. That was an automatic reaction that we will discuss later. But for some people, the stress reaction from such an event would have been so severe they would have needed to pull over and sit for twenty minutes to calm down. Then they would have worried for a week about what might have happened. Such individuals would have experienced significantly more stress than I did."

The Modern Pressure Cooker

As Sue listened, she realized that the majority of her stress that day had been unnecessary. She had overreacted a number of times and had wasted much energy. She consciously decided that she would be more cautious in the future.

"There are other factors that determine how much stress you experience," the speaker continued. "First, there's the unique you. We all relate to stressors differently. What may be a major stressor for me may be only a minor one for you. A second factor is your coping skills. Whether a specific stressful event is beneficial or harmful will depend in large measure on your coping skills. Dr. Peter Hanson says it well in his book *The Joy of Stress*." From the screen the audience read,

> **Stress can be fantastic. Or it can be fatal. It's all up to you.**
> **As well as respecting the dangers of stress,**
> **you can learn to harness its benefits.**

The instructor continued. "Whether the stress of your life is positive and productive or negative and unproductive depends on how well you develop coping skills that work with your uniqueness. This class is designed to help you with this process and it is vitally important that you are here for each of the following four sessions. Stress management is a process. We will always have stress. We need stress. We want stress. The key is to manage it effectively for optimum benefit."

Who Or What Heats Up Your Soup?

Cindy continued. "We must take a brief look at some major contemporary stressors. We all have a number of stressors that have been with us since there was life on the planet. There are, however, a few that are unique to present-day life, especially to the last few decades.

"The first is information and technology overload. We live in the information age. Information is increasing at such a rate that no one can keep up! No one can keep abreast of all the new information, even in small, specialty areas. There was a time, several hundred years ago, when a well-educated person knew just about all there was to know.

Not so today! We are forced to learn how to manage information rather than to master it. This information explosion is a major stressor and it is helpful to know that everyone is in the same boat and that no one is keeping up! All this information creates a multitude of new opportunities and can be very positive, but we need to be aware that it can also be a major stressor."

Bob looked at Sue and whispered, "No wonder I can't help the kids with their math. This also explains why they're doing work in junior high that I didn't even do in college."

"Fed by the information and technology explosion is the second major contemporary stressor: constant rapid change." The instructor flashed a new slide on the screen as Bob and Sue refocused on the lecture. "We are creatures of habit and even with a positive attitude toward change, it becomes one of our major stressors. It's especially true today because the pace of change is so fast and constant. For example, you finally learn a new computer program and it is, in fact, saving you much time and energy. Then suddenly, there is a new version or upgrade that puts your learning curve back to the beginning."

For a few moments, Sue let her mind wander as she reviewed the major changes in her life over the last few months. She had never thought of them as stressors because they were mostly positive changes—the new house, her decision to quit her job and work part-time with Bob so she could spend more time with the children, her parents getting older and moving closer. The list went on and on.

"Constant rapid change leads to our third major contemporary stressor—decisional overload." Sue tuned in again when she heard the words *decisional overload*. "Decisions, decisions, decisions," Cindy said with emphasis. "They come constantly and relentlessly and it seems they are also more complicated as our society becomes more complex. Someone has estimated that we can be bombarded with up to one thousand advertising messages in a single day! Of course, we can deal with only a small number of these but the process creates a degree of stress.

"A stress buffer that is very helpful with decisional overload is to take a *media fast* for at least one day a week and, occasionally, for a week or two at a time. At least take a break from news or listen very selectively to news reports, because one can easily get the sense that the world is totally out of control when all we are hearing is the bad news. This is especially important for people who tend to be prone to anxiety.

"You know you are experiencing decisional overload when someone innocently says, *What are we having for dinner?* and your response is *I don't know and I don't care. It's okay with me if we have Corn Flakes without the milk just so long as I don't have to decide!* A ripple of understanding laughter spread through the audience as Bob and Sue looked knowingly at each other.

"Finally, there is the daily hassle factor which has always been with us, but it seems to be magnified by technology and the speed of life today. Here are a few daily hassle laws that you may find interesting." Cindy put a list up on the screen. The group followed and laughed as she read them.

- **Balance's Law:** How long a minute is depends on which side of the bathroom door you're on.
- **Bedfellow's Rule:** The one who snores will fall asleep first.
- **Kovac's Conundrum:** When you dial a wrong number you never get a busy signal.
- **Fischer's Finding:** Sex is hereditary. If your parents never had it, chances are you won't either.
- **Gold's Law:** If the shoe fits, it's ugly.
- **Lawrey's Law:** If it jams, force it. If it breaks, it needed replacing anyway.
- **Crane's Rule:** There are three ways to get something done: do it yourself, hire someone, or forbid your kids to do it.

As the final laughter subsided, Cindy continued. "While constant change and the fast pace of life is exciting, the result can be serious overstimulation and imbalance. To get started in your workbook, list the primary pressure points of your life—the stressors. When finished, take a few minutes and discuss them with someone sitting near you. This will take us up to the break, and when we return we'll find out just how hot your stress soup is!"

Who Or What Heats Up My Soup?

1. _____

2. _____

3. _____

4. _____

5. _____

Stress Management Principles

• Pinpoint and recognize the main stress producers in your life and take appropriate action—now!

How Hot Is The Soup?

Measuring the temperature of your stress soup

WITHIN minutes of receiving the pressure points assignment, small groups of two to four began buzzing all across the auditorium. The time passed quickly, with the break providing a needed stretch and refreshment. When Cindy called the group back together she said, "At this point, two things are very important for us to understand. First, how the stress response affects our bodies generally, and second, how it affects you specifically.

"Whenever we perceive a threat or become excited, our body reacts immediately and automatically. The degree and intensity of the reaction depends upon the individual. Years ago, Dr. Walter Cannon conducted a classic experiment which illustrates very well what happens inside us when confronted by a stressful event.

"A cat's vital functions were monitored and its reactions studied when it was confronted by a dog. Two hormones were immediately released into the cat's system: adrenalin and noradrenalin. Instantaneously, the cat's blood circulation sped up; more energy-rich sugar appeared in its blood; blood-clotting mechanisms were accelerated; muscle function and breathing sped up; blood cells were released from storage depots into circulation; senses became keener and, meanwhile, the digestive system went into temporary inaction. The cat was prepared to fight or run, and these changes in body chemistry enhanced the cat's likelihood of survival under stress.

"Many additional studies have since been done and it is clear that this same _fight or flight_ mechanism works very similarly in us every time we get excited. However, seldom in today's world can we either fight or run. Your boss or spouse would not appreciate it, if every time you sensed a threat or were confronted, you hit someone or ran out the door.

"So what do we do? We sit. We smolder. We worry. We get frustrated. We may even scream. But it is not enough. The tension builds for hours or days, maybe even years. If there is no acceptable release, we suffer the devastating effects of stress illness."

Sue reviewed her hectic life, not only for that day but for all the months and years of stress they had lived through. _Life has been very good to us_, she thought, _but the stress of running a modern business and a home has really taken its toll, especially on Bob._

The Stress Test

"It's time to see how well you're managing your stress and how stress is affecting you," the instructor continued. "At this point, we have two simple assessment exercises for you to do. The first is the Stress Test. Turn to it now in your workbook and mark the answers based on the past month. Do not think too long on each question. Relax! Your score is neither good nor bad; it is not a pass/fail test. It simply gives you some indication as to how well you are coping with your stress. Let's take a few minutes now to do it."

Bob was well into the exercise before the instructor finished with the directions. As usual, he was one of the first to finish. "Sue!" he whispered fearfully, "if this is accurate, I'm in serious trouble! Just look at my score. It indicates serious distress!"

By the time Sue finished, Bob was antsy and needed a smoke. As most seminar participants were still working on the test, he sneaked out for a quick puff. Sue studied her results and was amazed at how well she was managing her stress. Improvement was possible but her score was very respectable—in the *positive well-being* range. *A pleasant surprise*, she thought.

Bob returned just as the seminar presenter began a discussion of the Stress Test results. He was amazed and a bit relieved by the large number of people who had results similar to his. "I guess I'm not the only one in trouble," he whispered to Sue. "I hope they have some answers here." Bob often *had* to talk, even in a meeting.

A number of participants were surprised by their score. Some, like Sue, were pleasantly surprised that they were handling their stress better than they thought. Others understood for the first time that stress was having a more negative effect on them than they had realized. After answering a number of questions about the Stress Test and the meaning of different scores, Cindy recommended that participants use the Stress Test periodically to monitor their stress levels.

Then she continued. "The body responds to excessive stress with a number of stress-warning signals. In your workbooks, check off any of the stress-warning signals that you are experiencing. Based on your previous test scores, I know that many of you are having a number of these stress signals. Any of these symptoms that are unusual for you may be an indicator of excessive stress."

"Whoa!" said Bob out loud, forgetting all the people around him. "I never realized how much stress was affecting me. This explains my almost constant headaches, sleeplessness, reduced effectiveness at the office, edginess, limited creativity, among a lot of other things. It's amazing I'm still able to function!"

A number of people around the room quietly began discussing their results. It was obvious that many were shocked at finding out the reason for many of their concerns. Sue had only a few negative signals but enough to alert her to begin coping with stress more effectively.

The instructor interrupted the chatterers. "Stress signals are the body's way of alerting you that it's in overload and you need to take action to resolve the problem before it gets worse. Ignoring these body warnings can result in serious illness and burnout.

"Let me illustrate with a story of a friend who had been overworking for a number of years. A number of stress signals were evident for some time but he did not recognize them as such. Suddenly, one afternoon, he started to shake uncontrollably. This lasted for about six hours, then disappeared as quickly as it began. Had he recognized this for what it was, it could have helped him identify stress as a major negative factor in his life. He then could have taken appropriate action to slow down and, had he done so, he may have prevented the extreme burnout that followed.

"In summary, learn to listen to your body, and give it the attention it needs to function effectively. Now, let's move on to learning how to cool off the soup."

Stress Management Principles

- Pinpoint and recognize the main stress producers in your life and take appropriate action—now!

- Develop an awareness of how stress is affecting you and listen to your body's stress-warning signals.

Stress-Warning Signals

Check Any Symptoms That Are Unusual For You.
They May Be An Indicator Of Stress.

Physical Signals

- ○ Headaches
- ○ Racing heart
- ○ Back pain
- ○ Dizziness
- ○ Indigestion
- ○ Tiredness
- ○ Restlessness
- ○ Tight neck, shoulders
- ○ Stomachaches
- ○ Sweaty palms
- ○ Sleep difficulties
- ○ Ringing in ears

Behavioural Symptoms

- ○ Bossiness
- ○ Attitude critical of others
- ○ Grinding of teeth at night
- ○ Overeating; excessive alcohol intake
- ○ Inability to get things done
- ○ Reduced interest in sex

Emotional Symptoms

- ○ Crying for no good reason
- ○ Boredom—no meaning to life
- ○ Feeling powerless to change things
- ○ Anger
- ○ Loneliness
- ○ Nervousness, anxiety
- ○ Edginess—ready to explode
- ○ Overwhelming sense of pressure
- ○ Unhappiness for no reason
- ○ Easily upset

Cognitive Symptoms

- ○ Trouble thinking clearly
- ○ Inability to make decisions
- ○ Loss of sense of humour
- ○ Memory loss
- ○ Forgetfulness
- ○ Thoughts of escape/running away
- ○ Lack of creativity
- ○ Constant worry

Relational Signals

- ○ Isolation
- ○ Intolerance
- ○ Resentment
- ○ Lashing out
- ○ Clamming up
- ○ Nagging
- ○ Lack of intimacy
- ○ Hiding
- ○ Mistrust

Spiritual Signals

- ○ Emptiness
- ○ Loss of meaning
- ○ Unforgiving attitude
- ○ Martyrdom complex
- ○ Loss of direction
- ○ Cynicism
- ○ Apathy
- ○ Doubt
- ○ Bitterness

The Stress Test

One measure of stress that has been used with success in national surveys is the General Well-Being Scale (GWB), designed by the National Centre for Health Statistics. A high score on the GWB represents an absence of bad feelings and expression of positive feelings.

The General Well-Being Scale Instructions: The following questions ask how you feel and how things have been going for you during the past month. For each question, fill in the circle next to the answer that most nearly applies to you. Since there are no right or wrong answers, it's best to answer each question quickly, without pausing too long on any of them.

1. How have you been feeling in general?
   5 ○ In excellent spirits
   4 ○ In very good spirits
   3 ○ In good spirits mostly
   2 ○ Up and down in spirits
   1 ○ In low spirits mostly
   0 ○ In very low spirits

2. Have you been bothered by nervousness or your "nerves"?
   0 ○ Extremely so—to the point where I can't work or take care of things
   1 ○ Very much so
   2 ○ Quite a bit
   3 ○ Some—enough to bother me
   4 ○ A little
   5 ○ Not at all

3. Have you been in firm control of your behaviour, thoughts, emotions, feelings?
   5 ○ Yes, definitely so
   4 ○ Yes, for the most part
   3 ○ Generally in control
   2 ○ Not too well in control
   1 ○ No, and I am somewhat disturbed
   0 ○ No, and I am very disturbed

National Center for Health Statistics

4. Have you felt so sad, discouraged, or hopeless, or had so many problems that you wondered if anything was worthwhile?

- 0 ○ Extremely so—to the point I have just about given up
- 1 ○ Very much so
- 2 ○ Quite a bit
- 3 ○ Some—enough to bother me
- 4 ○ A little bit
- 5 ○ Not at all

5. Have you been under or felt you were under any strain, stress, or pressure?

- 0 ○ Yes—almost more than I could bear
- 1 ○ Yes—quite a bit of pressure
- 2 ○ Yes—some, more than usual
- 3 ○ Yes—some, but about usual
- 4 ○ Yes—a little
- 5 ○ Not at all

6. How happy, satisfied, or pleased have you been with your personal life?

- 5 ○ Extremely happy—couldn't be more satisfied or pleased
- 4 ○ Very happy
- 3 ○ Fairly happy
- 2 ○ Satisfied—pleased
- 1 ○ Somewhat dissatisfied
- 0 ○ Very dissatisfied

7. Have you had reason to wonder if you were losing your mind, or losing control over the way you act, talk, think, feel, or of your memory?

- 5 ○ Not at all
- 4 ○ Only a little
- 3 ○ Some, but not enough to be concerned
- 2 ○ Some, and I've been a little concerned
- 1 ○ Some, and I'm quite concerned
- 0 ○ Much, and I'm very concerned

8. Have you been anxious, worried, or upset?

0 ○ Extremely so—to the point of being sick, or almost sick

1 ○ Very much so

2 ○ Quite a bit

3 ○ Some—enough to bother me

4 ○ A little bit

5 ○ Not at all

9. Have you been waking up fresh and rested?

5 ○ Every day

4 ○ Almost every day

3 ○ Fairly often

2 ○ Less than half the time

1 ○ Rarely

0 ○ None of the time

10. Have you been bothered by any illness, bodily disorder, pain, or fears about your health?

0 ○ All the time

1 ○ Most of the time

2 ○ A good bit of the time

3 ○ Some of the time

4 ○ A little of the time

5 ○ None of the time

11. Has your daily life been full of things that are interesting to you?

5 ○ All the time

4 ○ Most of the time

3 ○ A good bit of the time

2 ○ Some of the time

1 ○ A little of the time

0 ○ None of the time

National Center for Health Statistics

12. Have you felt downhearted and blue?

- 0 ○ All of the time
- 1 ○ Most of the time
- 2 ○ A good bit of the time
- 3 ○ Some of the time
- 4 ○ A little of the time
- 5 ○ None of the time

13. Have you been feeling emotionally stable and sure of yourself?

- 5 ○ All the time
- 4 ○ Most of the time
- 3 ○ A good bit of the time
- 2 ○ Some of the time
- 1 ○ A little of the time
- 0 ○ None of the time

14. Have you felt tired, worn out, used up, or exhausted?

- 0 ○ All the time
- 1 ○ Most of the time
- 2 ○ A good bit of the time
- 3 ○ Some of the time
- 4 ○ A little of the time
- 5 ○ None of the time

Note: For each of the four scales below, the words at each end describe opposite feelings. Circle any number along the bar that seems closest to how you have felt generally during the past month.

15. How concerned or worried about your health have you been?

Not concerned at all   Very concerned

| 10 | 8 | 6 | 4 | 2 | 0 |

National Center for Health Statistics

16. How relaxed or tense have you been?

Very relaxed   Very tense

| 10 | 8 | 6 | 4 | 2 | 0 |

17. How much energy, pep, and vitality have you felt?

Very energetic,   No energy at all,
   dynamic   listless

| 10 | 8 | 6 | 4 | 2 | 0 |

18. How cheerful or depressed have you been?

Very cheerful   Very depressed

| 10 | 8 | 6 | 4 | 2 | 0 |

Directions: Add up all the points you've checked or circled for each question and write your **Total Score Here:**

Total Stress Score	Stress State
81 – 110	Indicates Positive Well-Being
76 – 80	Low Positive
71 – 75	Marginal
56 – 70	Indicates Stress Problem
41 – 55	Indicates Distress
26 – 40	Serious
0 – 25	Severe

National Center for Health Statistics

Let The Soup Sit

Controlling the stress response

I**T** had been a long, difficult day for both Bob and Sue, and weariness was beginning to take its toll. Sue's concentration was beginning to wane but she knew some of the most important information of this evening's seminar was still to come. She decided that for next week's session, she must be more rested and relaxed. As her mind continued to wander, she thought, *Next time, Bob needs to get out of the office earlier. We could go out for dinner together before going to the seminar. Now that's a plan! We haven't had a full evening out for a while.*

Cindy had just finished answering a question and resumed the lecture as Sue refocused. "Up until now, we have been creating an awareness of how stress is affecting us. In the final two segments of tonight's session we will begin the process of finding practical solutions." Sue struggled to take it all in.

"I want you to have something useful that you can take home with you tonight and begin practicing this week, as you improve your stress-coping skills. One way to cool off the stress soup is to simply let it sit. One of the most important stress management principles is to learn to control the stress response. You can easily learn to do this and, with practice, it will greatly enhance your stress-coping skills.

"We briefly discussed the stress response—*flight or fight*—in the cat when threatened by a dog. Our bodies, however, do not differentiate between a positive and negative event. Any excitable event to which we react causes the body to release adrenaline, along with other hormones, into the blood stream. When this happens, the heart rate and circulation immediately speed up, blood pressure increases, breathing speeds up, muscles become tense, and there is more energy-rich sugar in the blood. A number of involuntary body reactions also prepare us to deal effectively with the situation.

"The body has sensed a challenge or threat and is prepared for action. This is good, and necessary at times. The problem is that daily living creates so many stressors in any given day that our bodies can easily become overloaded by producing too much adrenaline and other hormones. These extra hormones, when left circulating in the body, can cause serious illness. We must find ways to control and manage this response so it does not kill us!

"We will look at six ways to effectively control the stress response. The first is to **call a time out**. Or, as Stephen Covey puts it, *hit the pause button*. Simply let the soup sit. Move away from the situation for a while. Deliberately do not overreact. Go for a walk. Do something else. Walk away. Give yourself some space. Whatever it takes, do it!"

As the presenter paused to let her words sink in, Bob leaned over to Sue and whispered, "Now that's easier said than done, but it's definitely something I need to work on. My fuse has been short lately. I never realized how much energy I was wasting and, at the same time, causing myself unnecessary extra stress."

"Number two," Cindy continued, "is so simple that many people simply dismiss it. This could be likened to blowing on the soup to cool it off. As an immediate emergency measure, few things are as effective as this: **take three deep breaths**. The extra oxygen going throughout the body, and especially to the brain, produces an amazing relaxing effect. By the way, do you know how to take a deep breath? We all need a break. Let's stand up and practice this together."

With a little coaxing, everyone in the audience was on their feet. They listened carefully to Cindy's instructions and then breathed in through their noses and filled their lungs completely. They held it a few seconds, took in a little more air and then gently let it all out through their mouths. Following Cindy's lead, they did this three times.

Sue was amazed at how relaxing this little exercise was and, as she sat down, her mind was much clearer. While she was still tired, she could concentrate on the lecture more easily. Bob even looked more relaxed as he leaned over and said, "Now I think I can stay awake until the end of the session."

"You can do this little exercise almost anywhere, even while you are doing other tasks. Get into the habit and use it often," Cindy encouraged them.

"Number three is **analyze the situation and talk positively to** 3 **yourself.** Tell yourself, I can handle this. This reassurance will be relaxing and will give you the clarity of thought to deal with the situation without panic, thus reducing the stress response. Also, ask yourself the following questions: What can I do about this? (If nothing, then accept the situation and move on. If you can do something, then do it or at least begin the process toward a solution.) What difference will this make next year? Is it worth getting excited about? If so, get excited and react positively and deal with it. If not, leave it.

"Something else is very important. When analyzing the situation, identify the stressor, the cause of the problem. For instance, if it's a relationship issue, who or what is the stressor? Is it you? Is it someone else? Is it a unique circumstance? Find out and deal with it calmly and effectively."

This is good stuff, Bob thought. *Why haven't I come across this before? This is*

> **PRACTICAL TIPS for Letting the Soup Sit**
>
> - calling a time out
> - stepping back and observing
> - using affirmations
> - listening to your intuition
> - finding a place to give your gifts
> - viewing problems as opportunities
> - taking a media fast
> - avoiding perfectionism
> - cutting yourself some slack
> - knowing your limits
> - establishing boundaries
> - expressing yourself fully
> - setting realistic expectations
> - talking positively to yourself

practical material that I can use, beginning tomorrow. I must share this with Jim.

Cindy was moving on. "The fourth way to control the stress response is to **look for some humour in the situation**. We'll deal more fully with humour in stress management in another session. For now, I want you to start looking for humour in some of the stressful events that happen to you over the next week. Sometimes, the situation can be so ridiculously complex and challenging that it is comical in itself, if we can stand back and see it.

"Something that can reduce our overall reaction is number five: simply **admit your fallibility**. No one is perfect. So if you blew it, admit it and move on. Always being fearful of making a serious mistake is a major stressor in itself. Accept the fact that you will make mistakes and when you do, make them right and move on. Some individuals tend to be more perfectionistic than others. If this is you, cut yourself some slack and don't be so hard on yourself, or others, when you or they make mistakes.

"Finally, **do something easy and positive**. While you are letting a particular stressor cool off, do something that you are good at and enjoy. A friend called me one day and said in an excited voice, 'I'm burned out and need a vacation. I need to talk to you.' After a few minutes talking with him, I realized that he was very tired and needed a rest. The planned vacation was a good idea. But he was not in burnout. He was very tired, even exhausted. My counsel was to take a vacation and have a good rest. 'Enjoy the break,' I told him, 'and when you return, slow down, work fewer hours. Choose areas of your work that you especially enjoy, and concentrate on them for a few weeks. Allow your body to recover energy lost in the period of overwork.' This same principle works well when dealing with a difficult situation. Leave it alone for a while and do something that is easy and enjoyable for you. Then return and tackle the challenge, rested and refreshed, and you may be surprised at how much easier it is to deal with.

"Any questions on cooling off the soup before we go on to our final section for this evening?" After taking a few questions, Cindy moved quickly into the section on thinning the soup, recognizing that time was running out.

Stress Management Principles

- Pinpoint and recognize the main stress producers in your life and take appropriate action—now!

- Develop an awareness of how stress is affecting you and listen to your body's stress-warning signals.

- Learn to control the stress response by calling a time out, breathing deeply, analyzing the situation, looking for humour and cutting yourself some slack.

·

4

Thin The Soup

Mastering relaxation

BOB was getting restless. He was enjoying the seminar but, like Sue, was beginning to realize that to get the most out of it, he needed to be better prepared next time. *Next week, I'm going to leave work a bit early and have some diversion before coming*, he thought. Then he heard Cindy talking.

"Thinning the soup is closely related to letting the soup sit," she said. "The body's counterbalance to the stress response is the relaxation response. We can thin the soup or neutralize the effects of stress by learning how to activate and utilize the relaxation response for effective stress management.

"As Dr. Herbert Benson puts it, 'The relaxation response is an inborn set of physiological changes that offset the stress response.' While the stress response is involuntary and happens automatically, the relaxation response is voluntary and needs to be learned and practiced.

"In fact, the relaxation response can actually be used as a tool to counteract the harmful effects of today's stress. It is a scientific fact that while the stress response actually increases metabolism, heart rate, blood pressure, breathing rate, and muscle tension, as well as cholesterol levels, the relaxation response actually decreases these same functions.

"The good news is that we can learn to elicit the relaxation response whenever we wish. We simply need to understand the principle and the process and practice relaxation regularly. Relaxation is a conscious choice that needs to be practiced regularly.

"A couple of illustrations may be helpful. Relaxation could be compared to shifting a car down from overdrive. Life today can be very fast and we get accustomed to life in the fast lane. What we need is a relaxing, slower pace.

"Relaxing is often referred to as *letting go*. A simple story about a monkey well illustrates the dangers of hanging onto tensions that can kill us. To catch a monkey, one needs only to take a hollowed-out coconut shell. Drill a hole just large enough for a monkey to get its outstretched paw into it, and put a tempting piece of fruit or a bright-coloured object inside. The monkey will reach inside for the fruit or object and make a fist to clutch it. Not able to get the clenched fist out of the coconut shell and being unwilling to let go of its treasure, the monkey is caught in a trap of its own making. Like the monkey, we need to learn to *let go*. Continuing with this analogy, we can literally get the stress monkey off our back by learning to slow down and consciously give ourselves permission to relax."

Well, Bob mused, *I've definitely been living life in the fast lane. Relaxation has not been one of my strengths. I must learn how to relax and take life at a slower pace.* Bob looked at Sue just as she gave him a meaningful smile. They both knew that here was an idea whose time had come for them.

Activating The Relaxation Response

"A number of techniques will elicit the relaxation response," continued Cindy, after handling a number of comments and a question. "They include the following:

- **Regular deep breathing, using the diaphragm muscle**
- **Meditation or prayer**

- Progressive muscle relaxation
- Repetitive physical activity
- Repetitive word, thought, or prayer
- Visualization or imagery

"There are two basic components related to these techniques that make them most effective when using them. The first is a passive disregard for distracting thoughts, which means not worrying about how well you are doing.

"The second is a mental focusing device such as repeating a word, phrase, prayer, sound, or repetitive muscular activity to help shift your mind away from everyday thoughts and worries. When you notice yourself becoming distracted—caught up in some other train of thought —gently direct your mind back to your focus word or thought.

In this seminar, we are not able to spend much time practicing these techniques but if you make time for practice you can master them quite quickly. Should you need additional help in this area, there are classes available on relaxation, or you can read a good book on the subject.

"Notice in your workbooks, the basic steps in a relaxation sequence, as adapted from *The Wellness Book* by Dr. Herbert Benson and Eileen M. Stuart. Follow along as I read through the list:

1. Pick a focus word, phrase, image, or prayer.
2. Sit quietly in a comfortable position.
3. Close your eyes.
4. Relax your muscles.
5. Breathe slowly and naturally and, as you do so, repeat your focus word or phrase as you exhale.
6. Assume a passive attitude.
7. Continue for ten to twenty minutes.
8. Practice the technique once or twice daily.

When finished reading, Cindy said, "It's late, but we should take a few minutes for a quick practice. We won't take long, because within minutes you'll all be asleep. But we should do enough so you get the idea."

PRACTICAL TIPS for Thinning the Soup

- learning to relax
- taking regular stretch breaks
- getting a massage
- taking a hot bath
- getting a back rub
- smelling some flowers
- listening to peaceful music
- learning to simplify, simplify, simplify
- turning off the cell phone
- doing progressive muscle relaxation
- going with your natural rhythms
- having sex
- reading a book
- getting out into nature
- just sitting
- flying a kite
- practicing deep breathing
- working on a hobby
- meditating or praying
- relaxing at a red light
- letting the phone ring
- avoiding overstimulation
- controlling worry
- rubbing your hands and feet
- simply slowing down
- playing and having fun
- practicing regular relaxation
- getting a pet

She encouraged the group to put down their pens and workbooks and get into their most comfortable sitting position as she read quietly through the list. With the sudden quietness in the room, Sue almost drifted off to sleep as soon as she closed her eyes. With an embarrassing jerk, she woke up just as Cindy was saying, "Okay, this is short but it's as far as we can go tonight." Sue looked around, a bit embarrassed, but realized that nobody noticed her nap except Bob, who was enjoying the shocked look on her face. As Sue regained her composure, she winked at Bob and whispered, "I needed that little nap, so don't laugh."

"Several of you had a little nap," Cindy observed, as she began winding down the session. "That is a sign of relaxation and if we had continued much longer with that exercise at this hour, most of you would have fallen asleep. However, I also noticed that several of you could not relax. There could be a number of factors that would not allow you to relax here. Some of you will need to work at relaxation a bit harder than others before you master the skill.

"Well, it's time to wrap up this first session," Cindy announced. "I hope you've picked up something that you can begin using this week. Your homework, in preparation for next session, is to become more aware of how you are responding to events and to practice the relaxation response. In closing, I want to encourage you again to make it a priority to attend each session. This first session has been a bit long. The remaining sessions will be shorter and will focus on specific areas of stress management. Future sessions will also provide more time for group discussion and interaction. I will be around after this session ends if anyone has questions. Next week, our focus will be specifically on learning how to stir and play with the soup. Humour will definitely be a part of that session. You've been a great audience. See you next week."

After the applause, Bob and Sue made their way to the front, and Sue was one of the first to thank Cindy for the class. "We will definitely be here for each session," she assured Cindy. "We both need this class and I am sure we will have a number of questions later. Thanks so much for an excellent presentation."

"What a fine lady she is!" remarked Sue as they left the auditorium. "You know how you meet some people and you would like to get to know them better? Well, for me, Cindy is one of them."

"Once you get your stress under control and your priorities in order maybe you can get to know her better," Bob replied.

"I may just do that," Sue said as they got into the car.

Bob and Sue were quiet as they drove home, both too tired to talk. Or were they practicing the relaxation response? It had been a full day and they slept well that night.

Stress Management Principles

- Pinpoint and recognize the main stress producers in your life and take appropriate action—now!

- Develop an awareness of how stress is affecting you and listen to your body's stress-warning signals.

- Learn to control the stress response by calling a time out, breathing deeply, analyzing the situation, looking for humour and cutting yourself some slack.

- Learn the relaxation response and activate it often.

5

Stir The Soup

Exercising regularly

IT was three days after the stress seminar. Bob and Sue had returned to their busy schedules and had little time to discuss the session. It was Friday evening, Bob had not yet returned from work, and the children were all out on school functions. Sue decided that this was an excellent time to get some exercise.

A few years earlier, they had invested in good bikes for everyone. While they had used them a bit during vacations, the family had not really pursued cycling as they had planned. While Sue would ride occasionally, the kids' bikes definitely got the most use. Bob and Sue seldom got a chance to ride together, as it wasn't Bob's favourite physical activity. Bob actually didn't have a favourite physical activity— or he hadn't yet discovered it. After work he was a true *couch potato*.

Sue had biked enough to have a short route, taking about thirty minutes, and a longer, forty-five to fifty-minute route. She decided on the longer route as she was in no rush and had not been riding for some time. It was about 7 p.m. before Sue finally pedalled out of her driveway with about an hour of daylight left on that beautiful spring evening. Five houses down the street she saw their new neighbour getting out of her car. The house had recently sold and, with all the activity in their lives, neither Sue nor Bob had met the new people.

Sue was debating with herself whether to stop and talk, as daylight was fading, when suddenly the new lady turned and gave her a friendly wave. Sue recognized her. "Cindy," she said spontaneously, as she pulled her bike into the driveway. "You're from the stress seminar. Do you live here?"

"Yes," Cindy replied. "I just recently moved here. I knew you looked familiar when I saw you riding, but couldn't connect where we'd met. You attended the seminar on Tuesday. I remember now. You and your husband sat near the front."

"That's right!" Sue was excited. "We enjoyed the class very much and I have relaxed more this week than I usually do. Well, this is great having you as our new neighbour. We live just a few houses up the street. I look forward to getting to know you better."

"I see you're already *stirring the soup*," Cindy said.

"Stirring the soup?" Sue responded. "What do you mean?"

"I'm jumping ahead to our next seminar session when we'll talk about one of the best ways to manage stress, which is physical activity. It cools the soup by stirring and burning off the negative results of the stress response. Do you bike often?"

"Not as often as I would like. I can't seem to get the rest of the family together long enough to do it as a family. Hopefully, this seminar will help get Bob into exercise. I enjoy it more when I have company," Sue answered.

"I enjoy biking too but haven't had a chance to ride since moving. In fact, if you don't mind, I'd like to ride with you sometime." Cindy saw an opportunity to get acquainted with someone in her new neighbourhood.

"I'd be delighted," Sue replied. "If your bike is handy, why not come now? It's a beautiful evening. We still have about forty-five minutes of daylight."

"Just give me a minute to change and I'll be right with you."

What a pleasant surprise, thought Sue, as Cindy prepared for the ride. *A new neighbour who's into health and fitness. Just what we need!*

As Sue and Cindy enjoyed the evening ride, they also discovered a number of common interests and as they returned to their homes, both sensed that a very enjoyable and precious friendship had begun.

It was late Saturday afternoon before Bob and Sue had a good opportunity to talk and bring each other up to date. While Bob was pleased about their new neighbour, and Sue's developing friendship, Sue was impressed with Bob's progress in stress management. He'd already done some reorganizing at work and had allowed himself more free time, including leaving work by four on Tuesdays, the day of the seminar. He'd been seriously watching his stress responses and had tried practicing some relaxation. "This relaxation thing," he said, "will take some getting used to. When I try it, it seems like I'm wasting time and I can't seem to relax."

Tuesday came soon enough. Bob and Sue enjoyed a good breakfast as the family prepared for the day. Seldom was it possible for more than two of them to eat breakfast together. Sue, happy to see Bob slowing down long enough to eat a healthy breakfast, suggested that the two of them eat out for dinner and then go directly to the seminar. "Good idea," Bob agreed. "I plan to leave work early and be home by four o'clock. How about a short bike ride before going out, with the emphasis on *short*? I haven't done much exercise lately but I should get started. Did you say Cindy called this *stirring the soup*?"

"That's right," said Sue. "I can be home and ready by four. We haven't been biking together for months. Yes, it'll be great to *stir the soup* together!"

Returning home a little before four, Sue found Bob sound asleep on the sofa. *Well, this is strange*, she thought. *He never comes home early and he's not one to take a nap.*

Sue's arrival woke Bob. Before she could ask for an explanation he said, "Today was a bit slow at the office, so I decided to try out this relaxation thing. It wouldn't work for me at the office—too many distractions—so I came home about three, chose an inspirational thought, got comfortable and began systematically relaxing my body. I must have slept for nearly an hour. I actually relaxed!"

"You must have needed the extra sleep," Sue replied.

"Well, I do feel refreshed," Bob said. "I should be able to stay awake tonight."

The bike ride was delightful in the afternoon sunshine. In fact, they were enjoying it so much they went much farther than intended and by the time they got home, showered, and ready to go out, it was getting late. Dinner was delicious and enjoyable at a quiet restaurant near the Y. They decided that for the duration of the seminar, they would follow this same pattern, with only the nap in question.

As Bob and Sue arrived, relaxed and fresh, about fifteen minutes early for the seminar, Cindy was doing some final preparations. When she saw them, she came over, greeted them and remarked about how rested and relaxed they looked. Sue introduced Bob and shared a bit about their relaxing afternoon. As they took their seats and prepared for the seminar, the large hall filled quickly with excited and friendly people. It seemed to Sue that everyone looked more relaxed than last week, but then maybe it was just that she was not as tired and uptight.

Cindy was ready to begin. "Welcome to the second session of *Don't Eat The Soup As Hot As They Cook It!* I hope you had a good week and that you were more aware of your stress responses. Did anyone practice relaxation? How many actually made some adjustments this week?" she asked. "Raise your hand if you feel you made some progress."

Hands went up all across the auditorium and several people made a comment or asked a question. Cindy patiently answered all the questions, with Bob asking the last one. He shared his several unsuccessful relaxation attempts and his afternoon nap and asked, "Why did I fall asleep so fast and sleep so long? I never do that!"

"Most likely," Cindy replied, "your body finally got the message that you were giving it permission to relax. You were probably more tired than you realized and as you started to relax on the soft sofa, with no distractions, your body took advantage of the opportunity and had a power nap. There's nothing wrong with a power nap from time to time. Some people plan it into their schedule. Bob, how did you feel when you woke up?"

"Silly, and a bit guilty at first," he said. "You know what I mean— sleeping in the afternoon. But when I got fully awake, I felt great. In fact, I still feel more rested now than I did when I got up this morning."

"Sounds to me like you needed that sleep," Cindy commented. "Just keep working on those relaxation exercises and before long you will be able to relax and feel refreshed without actually falling asleep.

"Those were excellent questions and comments. It's obvious that some of you are making excellent progress. As we move into tonight's lecture, first I would like to share with you what I consider to be the ABC's of effective stress management," Cindy explained, as the big screen revealed the following:

Awareness and adaptability

Balance and flexibility

Control—using our power of choice

"As today's pressure cooker gets hotter and hotter and the stressors march on relentlessly," continued Cindy, "we must be aware of our personal stress levels and be conscious of how the stress is affecting us. It's wise, from time to time, to examine how well we're adapting and, when necessary, make whatever lifestyle changes we need to keep our life in proper balance.

"Living life in proper balance is the major challenge and a basic goal of effective stress management. Someone has said, 'Blessed are those who are flexible because they can't be bent out of shape!' Being flexible is a major asset in maintaining proper balance.

"Finally, control is vital. We have very little control over some stressors, like the untimely death of a loved one, or a serious illness or accident, but we do choose most of our stressors and we have a degree of control over them. The question is, do we exercise proper control and use our amazing power of choice to take the personal responsibility necessary? By the way, do you know the single most stressful situation? It's having 100% responsibility but very little control. If you find yourself in such a situation, you must make changes, and the sooner the better.

"Awareness, Balance and Control are the ABC's of stress management and the heart of this seminar. We simply want to be able to help you achieve these more effectively.

"We will now explore two very interesting and effective stress management tools to help you in cooling off the stress soup. First, open your workbook to the section entitled *Stirring The Soup*," Cindy continued. "You knew we had to deal with this subject sooner or later, didn't you? Yes, you guessed it—physical activity. The single best way to manage stress is physical exercise. After the break, we'll look at playing with the soup—humour and stress. So settle back, relax, and enjoy the learning process."

Both Bob and Sue were relaxed, rested, and ready to learn. They were motivated, and their small successes were just the catalyst they needed to keep going.

"How many of you are getting regular physical exercise? I mean three to five periods of aerobic exercise a week on a regular basis," the instructor explained. Only a few hands went up. After affirming those with good exercise habits, Cindy said, "It looks like most of this class are typical North Americans. Even with all the promotion of exercise in the media, still only a small minority, about 10–20% of the population, get adequate physical activity.

"Most people, it seems, have a number of good excuses, like humourist and survivor Barbara Johnson, who reports, 'I had to give up jogging for my health because my thighs kept rubbing together and setting my pantyhose on fire!' Others have bought into Mark Twain's advice. He said that when he got the urge to exercise he would just lie down and wait until the feeling passed. Bob Hope recommended a rigorous exercise regimen: 'Sit in the bathtub, pull the plug, and fight against the current!' Then there are those whose exercise philosophy is to start slow and then taper off."

The hearty laughter was both refreshing and relaxing. The audience was now prepared to take a hard look at the role of exercise in stress management.

Cindy emphasized this point: "Regular daily activity, for at least 30 minutes—if possible in the fresh air and sunshine—is one of your major tools for effective stress management. In fact, few people can manage their stress effectively without some form of physical exercise. While exercise is vital to controlling stress, it is one of the best habits to ensure overall health and wellness. Note this statement by a researcher named Bortz, in the *Journal of the American Medical Association*, as long ago as 1982:

There is no drug in current or prospective use that holds as much promise for sustained health as a lifetime program of physical exercise.

"Well," Bob whispered to Sue, "exercise like we had today has to become a regular habit. We need to start using those bikes more often—and as a family—wouldn't you say?" Sue nodded her agreement, knowing that if Bob was convinced, there was a good chance that it would happen.

"Modern science has isolated over fifty specific benefits of exercise on the body," Cindy continued. "You will find a partial list of thirty-five exercise benefits in your workbook. Take a quick look as I mention a few in each area. Note first some of the physical benefits: lowered cholesterol levels and blood pressure; increased energy, metabolism, and bone density; improved sleep, circulation, digestion, appearance; and a strengthened immune system.

"The mental and emotional benefits of exercise are also significant. They include reduced anxiety and stress, and even the relief of some depression. It improves your self-image and your sense of well-being. You also have a more positive sense of self-worth and better mental performance.

"Several of the major lifestyle diseases can also be prevented with regular exercise. These include the major killers: heart disease, cancer, osteoporosis, and obesity. A strengthened immune system, combined with the overall disease prevention—benefits that come from better circulation of oxygen and nutrients at the cellular level—is a major buffer against a variety of serious illnesses.

"Of course, the major benefit relating to stress is the fact that exercise is the simplest and best way of burning off the extra adrenaline and other hormones pumped into the bloodstream by the stress response. This is one of the primary reasons I like to do my exercising in the late afternoon or evening. If I've been doing mainly mental work all day, it clears out the mental cobwebs and burns off any extra stress hormones accumulated from the stress responses of my day."

That's a great idea, Sue thought, as she reviewed their family's average day. Mornings were always so busy and none of the family enjoyed getting up early. Where had she gotten the idea that morning was the best time to exercise? It definitely wasn't for her or anyone in her family.

"By the way," Cindy asked, "when is the best time to exercise for optimum health?"

"Early morning," someone answered, and a consensus quickly developed for morning. A few people ventured evening but suggested not right after dinner or just before bed.

"Very good," the instructor agreed. "Strenuous exercise just before bed isn't recommended as it may interfere with sleep. Also, heavy exercise too soon after a meal will interfere with proper digestion. But when is the overall best time for exercise? It's whatever time is best for you. More important than *when* you exercise is that you exercise *regularly*! Morning, noon, or night, or in between, the major benefits come from just doing it!

"A second question that we should deal with here is which exercise is best? Again, the answer is the one that is best for you. Which exercise do you enjoy most? For me, jogging is boring but I thoroughly enjoy cycling. While I jog or run once in a while, the core of my aerobic exercise program is cycling. You are more likely to exercise regularly if it is an exercise that you enjoy. So experiment. Find the type of exercise that you enjoy most and do it!

"The basic exercise principle to be aware of is that you need twenty to thirty minutes, at least, three to four times a week, of a good aerobic exercise, like running, swimming, cycling, or cross-country skiing, with some muscle-stretching exercises before and after. Doing muscle-*strengthening* exercises two to three times a week is also very beneficial and helps with muscle tone. As with the time of exercise, the type of exercise is not as important as just doing it! My message is *get moving, keep moving, and enjoy it.* Enjoying exercise is important. Recent research actually shows that mere toleration of exercise, the *I will do this if it kills me* attitude, is not as beneficial and, in some cases, may be positively harmful. So enjoy it!

"I actually recommend the target of daily exercise because if you target daily, you will more likely achieve the minimum of three to four times a week. Few, who target the minimum, actually achieve it."

Cindy stopped at this point and asked if there were any questions. She took several minutes to answer a number of good questions that both Sue and Bob found very helpful. Bob turned to Sue and said, "I've known much of this for years. What I need is some motivation. Come to think of it, recent circumstances are providing some motivation." Sue just listened and decided that she must not only see that she and Bob got regular exercise but the whole family too. She was already noticing how, as the children grew older, they were getting less and less physical activity. Television, computers, videos, and video games were replacing more creative and restorative recreation.

"We must talk a bit about motivation," Cindy continued. "You are obviously motivated to a degree, to handle your stress better, or you wouldn't be here. Regular physical exercise is essential to that goal. Plus all the additional benefits we discussed earlier. I like what Jim Rohn says about motivation." She looked up at the screen as she read:

The best motivation is self-motivation. The guy says, 'I wish someone would come by and turn me on.' What if they don't show up? You've got to have a better plan for your life.

"I heard a story recently that illustrates motivation," Cindy continued. "It seems that one of the churches on the East Coast needed to construct an addition. Those of you familiar with Eastern Canada and the United States know that many of the churches are surrounded by a cemetery and some graves lie quite close to the building. Well, as the workers were digging the foundation, they got a bit too close to the cemetery. One of the men was down in the trench when the wall caved in and some bones from a nearby grave fell into the hole.

"Immediately, the workman took off running as fast as he could for ten minutes. He didn't return to work for a week. When he finally showed up, the boss said, 'Where have you been all week?'

"The workman replied, 'Well, when I saw those bones, I just lost it and took off running as fast as I could for ten minutes.'

"'Ten minutes!,' the boss said. 'Where have you been all week?' The workman replied, 'Walking back!'"

As the laughter died down, Cindy said, "Now *that* is motivation! I hope some of you will get motivated to start or continue with regular exercise.

"Just before we take a break, I must provide some guidelines to the majority who are now motivated to get started. Here is something I adapted recently from the newsletter *Consumer Reports on Health,* called *7 Ways To Start An Exercise Habit And Stick With It!*

"First, **make it easy and start at your own pace**. The fitness world has finally got beyond the phase where everyone believed in the motto *no pain, no gain*. Today, we know that any physical activity is good for you and that, to a point, more is better. If, however, you have not done any serious exercise for years, you may need to check first with your physician. Just make sure you start off easy. Walking is an excellent exercise to begin with and even to continue as your favourite. Walking is an exercise that most people can do and it requires no special equipment. At first, you may only be able to walk between one or two telephone poles, but with persistence and regularity, before long you will be able to walk several kilometers at a good pace. In the beginning, beware of trying to keep up with someone else. Set your own pace at your fitness level and gradually build up. If you overdo it at first, you will get sore muscles and this may serve to convince you that exercise is not good for you.

"The second guideline is **eliminate the pain**. Keep your workouts safe and comfortable. A basic rule is, while exercising, you should be able to talk but not sing. If you are breathing heavily and sweating profusely, you are probably overdoing it. Yet, if you are taking a leisurely stroll through the park and can sing with the birds, then you need to speed up a bit. You should feel at least as good after you exercise as before you start. If you want to monitor your heart rate, it should be below seventy percent of its maximum, which is 220 minus your age."

Sue, who at one time had learned how to find and take her pulse, did a quick mental calculation and realized that now, for her and Bob, their maximum heart rate while exercising was not to exceed 180.

"Number three follows along with what we discussed a few minutes ago. **Make it fun.** Choose an activity you enjoy, and work out with a friend if you are at equal fitness levels," Cindy continued.

"Four is how you can get extra exercise throughout the day. Simply **squeeze in a variety of small activities during the day.** For instance, park at the far end of the parking lot at the mall, and take the stairs rather than the elevator. Watch for opportunities for a little extra exercise and take advantage of them.

"Number five is very important. **Get over the hump.** You will know that you're over the hump when you get to the point that when you don't exercise, you miss it as you would miss a meal. In fact, getting enough proper exercise is just as important as eating the right foods. It is unfortunate but true, that if you don't plan exercise and actually put it on your to-do list, you will just not get enough. Most of us do not naturally get enough exercise. Therefore, we need to have an exercise plan. My rule is for every three meals, get one bout of serious exercise and do not eat the fourth meal until exercise happens. For sure, you won't miss the meal, so the reminder to exercise will be very helpful. You will be over the hump after about three weeks of regular activity and you start recognizing the benefits.

"**Watch for subtle improvements** is number six. As you find yourself handling stress better, sleeping better, being more positive, and having more energy, you will be encouraged to stick with the program.

"Finally, **expect lapses.** From time to time, despite your best efforts, circumstances will overrule your exercise schedule. Take these in stride and resume your exercise routine as soon as possible. You may need to start slower after the delay, but do continue. Just because you've been sick for a week and haven't been able

PRACTICAL TIPS for Stirring the Soup

- exercising regularly
- digging in the garden
- taking a walk
- going to a gym
- hiking in the mountains
- taking the stairs
- working out intensely
- chopping wood
- cycling
- running or jogging
- parking at the far end of the lot
- swimming
- jumping for joy
- lifting weights
- skipping

to walk doesn't mean that you can't get back into fitness. If you can't eat for a week, does that mean you stop eating?

"It was W.C. Fields who said, 'There comes a time…when we must grab the bull by the tail and face the situation.' This is so true about exercise. So as Nike says, *Just do it!*

"Well, it's time for our break," Cindy concluded. "We have some refreshments and some of you may want to get outside for some fresh air and a short walk. We'll begin again in about twenty minutes and talk about playing with the soup."

Bob was in desperate need of a smoke. "Wow," he said. "I haven't had a smoke since before I left the office. It's now well after eight; that's over five hours without a smoke!" Sue was impressed. She couldn't remember the last time he had gone that long voluntarily. He even woke up sometimes in the night for a smoke.

As they picked up a glass of juice and walked out of the building, Bob commented, "I haven't even had a craving until just a few minutes ago. Maybe the nap, the exercise, and a relaxing evening—with healthy food and wonderful company—are good for me!"

"Well now, just maybe they are!" Sue responded as they met some old business acquaintances and began comparing notes.

Stress Management Principles

- Pinpoint and recognize the main stress producers in your life and take appropriate action—now!

- Develop an awareness of how stress is affecting you and listen to your body's stress-warning signals.

- Learn to control the stress response by calling a time out, breathing deeply, analyzing the situation, looking for humour and cutting yourself some slack.

- Learn the relaxation response and activate it often.

- Get regular daily physical activity.

6

Play With The Soup

Using humour

BOB and Sue spent the break visiting with long-time business acquaintances but they also met some new people. With all the visiting and discussion, the twenty minutes flew by and soon they heard the call, "It's time to get started again."

When the majority had settled in their seats, Cindy began. "For the rest of our session tonight we are going to explore one of the most fun and powerful of stress buffers. In the delightful book entitled *Lighten Up*, humour is defined as *a set of survival tools that relieve tension, keeping us fluid and flexible instead of allowing us to become rigid and breakable, in the face of relentless change.* As we discussed last week, constant rapid change is one of our most challenging, contemporary stressors. Tonight, we will discover humour as one of the major antidotes for the stresses of life. Note these quotes about humour and fun." On the big screen, the audience followed as Cindy read:

- **There ain't much fun in medicine, but there's a heck of a lot of medicine in fun.**

  — Josh Billings

- Humour is one of the truly elegant defenses of the human repertoire. Few would deny that the capacity for humour, like hope, is one of mankind's most potent antidotes for the woes of Pandora's box.
  — George Vaillant

- If you wish to glimpse inside a human soul and get to know a man ... just watch him laugh. If he laughs well, he's a good man.
  — Dostoevsky

- The joy of joys is the person of light but unmalicious humour.
  — Emily Post

- A smile on your face is a light to tell people that your heart is at home.
  — Allen Klein

"Here are a couple of fun medical facts about humour," Cindy continued. "Dr. William Fry Jr. has shown in studies that just twenty seconds of laughter is the cardiovascular equivalent of three minutes of strenuous rowing. Someone then calculated that a hundred laughs are equal to ten minutes on a rowing machine. Others have discovered that ten minutes of laughter is equal to two hours of sleep, and only fourteen minutes of laughter equals the relaxing effect of eight hours of meditation."

This is great, thought Bob. *Now I understand why I used to feel better and even more relaxed after reading or hearing a funny story or watching a funny movie. But it doesn't work that way anymore. Maybe I'm too uptight and have been taking life too seriously. I need to dig out some of my old joke books.*

"Humour is definitely a powerful stress buffer," continued Cindy. "Research shows that people who use humour regularly suffer less fatigue, tension, anger, depression, and confusion in response to stress. In fact, Dr. Lee Berk, of Loma Linda University School of Medicine, has showed that, just as the anticipation of stress can trigger the stress response, the converse is also true, that the anticipation of pleasure can trigger a stress buffer.

"It's true that humour comes easier for some people than others. But here is the good news: humour is not a gift. It's a learned skill. That means it's totally under your control and can be perfected through regular, repeated use."

Sue was fascinated by this information. She had always admired Bob's terrific sense of humour but, recently, he seemed to have lost it. She wondered why, but couldn't pin down the reason.

Cindy went on. "There are a number of ways that humour counteracts the negative effects of stress. In your workbook, please fill in some of the answers. First, humour gives you a break from ongoing stress and helps you buy time for creatively altering the stress response. It also encourages the relaxation response. Second, humour restores and replenishes depleted emotional reserves. Third, it enhances the immune system and lowers blood pressure.

"The fourth benefit of humour, in counteracting the stress response, is a very interesting one. A good belly laugh is actually a form of internal jogging which releases endorphins into the system. Endorphins are a group of *feel good* hormones that are natural painkillers. They are released into the system in at least two ways. One is a good belly laugh and another is regular physical exercise. Endorphins have an effect on the body that is similar to morphine. They are natural drugs—inexpensive and legal!

"A final benefit of humour, as a counterbalance for stress, is that it helps prevent hardening of the attitudes. It keeps us playful and fun-loving, and contributes to a positive mental attitude.

"At this point, I want to share with you a couple of jokes that always make me laugh. While I am sharing these, think of a couple of good, clean jokes that *you* can share just before we close. People and circumstances are one of the best sources of good humour, and children can be especially funny without realizing it.

"As the story goes, a small boy was standing with his dad in a line at the bank. There was an especially tall and very broad woman in front of them. The lady went to the teller and completed her business. Just as she was putting the last of her papers away, a beeper on her belt went off: *Beep, beep, beep*. The little boy shouted, 'Watch out, dad! She's backing up!'"

The joke really hit the funny bone of the group, and all had a good laugh. It especially worked on Bob, who was caught totally off guard. He was still wiping tears from his eyes as Cindy continued. "A little girl asked her grandma one day, 'How old are you?' The grandmother was taken aback and said, 'Sweetheart, you never ask an adult, especially a lady, how old she is. It's not polite.' Then the little girl asked, 'Grandma, how much do you weigh?'

"Again grandma said, 'You never ask an adult how much they weigh. It's not polite.' Then the girl went off to play, and sometime later returned all excited and announced, 'Grandma I know how old you are and how much you weigh. You are sixty-five years old and you weigh one hundred and forty pounds.' Surprised, grandma said, 'How did you know that?' The little girl said, 'Well, I was digging around in your purse and found your driver's license and I also discovered that you got an F in sex.'"

Again, the group had a good belly laugh. You could almost feel everyone relax and enjoy the change. "We'll share with you a number of things that'll tickle your funny bone during the next three sessions and I'm sure you've already discovered some of the stress busters in your workbook. Start looking for some good clean jokes and bring them to each session to share with your group. Before we divide into groups for our last assignment this evening, we need to look at the section in your workbook called *Creating A Humour Survival Kit*. This can be one of your best defenses against stress, as it contains a number of useful stress busters. Note the following guidelines:

1. **Begin immediately, a collection of good humour**. Antidotes, cartoons, joke books, humourous audio and videotapes, et cetera, that make you laugh. Then visit your collection often, especially when life seems to be getting a bit difficult.

2. **Begin immediately, a list of all your blessings**, including all the people and events that have brought you joy. Again, review the list often and, for maximum benefit, do it right after eliciting the relaxation response.

3. **Celebrate life and be absorbed in the moment**. Humour comes when you keep a lookout for it and are fully present and aware. Be alert and watch for humour.

4. **Stay in touch with your inner child**. Exercise your imagination often and adopt an attitude of playfulness. It has been said, *A great man is one who doesn't lose the child within.*

5. **Don't take yourself, or life, too seriously.** As George Burns put it, *You can't help getting older, but you don't have to get old.*

"Let's review. Tonight, we have touched briefly on two very important stress-coping tools. Regular physical activity and a good sense of humour are both indispensable as you cool off and keep your stress soup manageable. Your assignments for this week are (1) to begin or continue physical activity and (2) to explore the humourous and playful components of your life.

"Now, we want to give you an opportunity to act on the information you have learned tonight and share it with the members of your group. From now on, we'll do this at the end of each session. It's one of the most beneficial parts of the course.

"First of all, turn to this page in your workbook." Cindy flashed the following on the screen:

Improving The Recipe For A Better Soup

My Action Plan For This Week

• **Start:** _____

• **Stop:** _____

• **Keep:** _____

"Looking back over last week's session and tonight's, let's review the four key stress management principles we have discussed. Last week, we looked at controlling the stress response and eliciting the relaxation response. Tonight, we've covered regular physical activity and humour. Now it's decision time! Write in the blank beside *Start*, one thing that you're going to start doing immediately to manage your stress better. Then beside *Stop*, one thing you are going to immediately stop doing because it's not helping you manage your stress. Finally, because we have all survived and done some things right, write beside *Keep*, something you are going to keep doing because it's been helping you manage your stress effectively. Take a few minutes to complete this exercise."

The room became quiet as the class went to work on the assignment. Both Bob and Sue wrote *exercise* beside *Start*, which simply reinforced their recent decision to become more physically active. Bob struggled with the *Stop*, knowing that to stop smoking would be his best response, but realizing that the time was not right to quit, he wrote *overworking*, and beside *Keep,* he wrote *sense of humour.*

"Good," whispered Sue, looking over at Bob's workbook. "I'm going to *Stop* procrastinating and plan my days better, with more time for relaxation, and *Keep* working part-time."

"Okay," Cindy said, after about five minutes. "Let's divide into groups of four to six individuals. I have two assignments for you. First of all, after you've introduced yourselves, share two or three short, clean jokes to get relaxed as a group. Then share and discuss what you wrote in the decision exercise. We have about twenty minutes. I'll call you back together for some closing remarks."

The room began to buzz again. Cindy and her helpers made sure that everyone was in a group and that the groups were not too large. Bob and Sue teamed up with a couple they'd met during the break. They learned that Dale was a teacher at the local community college and Pam was a nurse. She was very active in municipal politics and was currently serving both as a ward representative and deputy mayor. They were only a few years younger than Bob and Sue, and had children that were just beginning school.

Within minutes, loud laughter floated across the room as the participants began relaxing and telling jokes. Bob and Sue, with their new friends, shared several jokes. *Bob's becoming more like his old self*, Sue thought, as she watched him. He was just about to tell another joke when Cindy interrupted the class.

"Very good!" she said. "We've got the endorphins flowing. Let's keep some good jokes for next week. Now discuss your decisions for action."

The room quieted somewhat as more serious discussions began. Later, when Cindy closed the discussions, Bob asked Sue, "Have two hours gone already? It seems we just got started."

Cindy wrapped up with a few announcements and encouraged everyone to make the sessions a priority and to be present for each one. It seemed, from Sue's observation, that almost everyone was back this week, plus a few more.

"Next week, we'll look at two very important stress-coping tools—making sure the soup is nutritious and becoming aware of any poison in the soup. See you then, and have a great week."

Following the sincere and gracious applause, Bob and Sue visited with their new friends, Dale and Pam, for a few minutes. They exchanged phone numbers and agreed to keep in touch through the week. Sue noticed that Pam seemed to be experiencing more negative stress than Dale, but both were tense and uptight.

Sue wanted to speak to Cindy, as she had a couple of questions, but there was already a large number of people around her. Sue decided to visit her at home or invite her on a bike ride. How fortunate to have her as a neighbour!

After visiting with a number of people, Bob and Sue finally reached their vehicle and started home. "Whoa," Bob said. "This

PRACTICAL TIPS for Playing with the Soup

- using humour
- laughing at yourself
- going to watch a stand-up comic
- having some fun
- reading a funny book
- renting a comedy video
- celebrating life
- enjoying the moment
- reading the newspaper comics
- listing all your blessings
- not taking yourself too seriously
- not taking life too seriously
- staying in touch with the child within
- reviewing your blessing list often
- using your humour survival kit
- throwing a party
- playing a board game with your family

has been a great evening! I really needed that reinforcement to exercise—and permission to be silly again!"

"Well," said Sue playfully, "you don't need to be as silly as you once were but I'm glad you're getting your sense of humour back!"

Later, in bed, they talked about their progress and plans. They sketched out an exercise plan that would mesh with family schedules. They would attempt some exercise together a couple of times a week and, hopefully, at least once a week with the whole family. Beyond that, they would have to be on their own. It had been a good day and a much better week. Bob put it this way: "We're in a long tunnel but I'm beginning to see a small light flickering at the other end."

Stress Management Principles

- Pinpoint and recognize the main stress producers in your life and take appropriate action—now!

- Develop an awareness of how stress is affecting you and listen to your body's stress-warning signals.

- Learn to control the stress response by calling a time out, breathing deeply, analyzing the situation, looking for humour and cutting yourself some slack.

- Learn the relaxation response and activate it often.

- Get regular daily physical activity.

- Humour is a wonderful stress buffer. Begin immediately to create a humour survival kit and use it regularly.

7

Make Sure The Soup Is Nutritious

Eating wisely for strength, energy, and endurance

WITH a groan, Bob Picco crawled out of bed the next morning. "I ache all over," he announced, as he stumbled into the bathroom.

"I was afraid we were overdoing the exercise yesterday," Sue said. "Maybe we rode too far. We're not in shape yet."

"I'm definitely *out* of shape!" Bob agreed. "I have all these aching muscles that I didn't even know I had. The obvious conclusion? Exercise is *not* good for me. How do you feel?"

"Not bad. The pain will only last a couple of days. Take a hot and cold shower. That'll get the circulation going."

As Bob turned on the shower, he thought, *Yes, I want to try that cold shower thing again, this time under my control.*

A few minutes later Sue heard, "Whoa! Is that cold!" For Bob, this was major progress.

Bob came to breakfast still sore but very alert. He was quite proud of himself. "I'm going to do that every morning for a while. After that experience, I don't need a cup of coffee or even a smoke to wake me up!"

Once the family was out for the day, Sue decided to call Cindy. After getting answers to her questions from the night before, she suggested they pack a lunch and go for a bike ride in the local park. Cindy agreed. They were well into the heart of the park by lunch time and stopped at one of Sue's favourite spots and ate their lunch.

"What a beautiful spot!" Cindy said. "This part of town is new to me and I really appreciate having you show me around."

"My pleasure," responded Sue. "It's not every day that I get the opportunity to have a friend who can answer my lifestyle questions while exercising. Their friendship deepened as they ate lunch in the gorgeous spring setting. It was relaxing and enjoyable for both of them.

As they prepared to leave, Cindy remarked, "I was glad to see that you and Bob teamed up with Dale and Pam during the group session last night. I've been working with Pam for some time, on a personal basis. Her stress levels are very high right now and she needs someone like you with whom to share her experiences. Maybe as you get to know her better, you could become a key person in her developing support system."

"I'd be glad to help," responded Sue. "I noticed that she was very tense and uptight last night."

"She's at a very busy time in her life," Cindy continued. "Over-commitment and overwork are her major challenges at present. I'm especially concerned with her lack of stress-coping skills and reserves, but her personal support system is also weak. Dale, her husband, is very supportive and they seem to have a strong marriage. With three small children, and working full-time, and being involved in politics, it seems she's trying to be a superwoman. I feel tired just talking to her about her daily schedule. In addition, she has no close relatives living in town and has few, if any, close friends. She is a classic case for developing burnout. I've been looking for someone who might be able to develop a supportive friendship with her. Now, with both of you in the same group, you may be able to get close enough to help her."

"Thanks for the insight. I'll try to get to know her better and see if I can be of help," Sue assured. "I know what it's like to have small children and to be working full-time. It's just plain tough!"

They enjoyed the ride home and, before going their separate ways, agreed to make it a weekly event, as it was a good time for Sue and the only time for Cindy.

The rest of the week flew by. The Picco family managed a short family bike ride on Sunday afternoon. Everyone enjoyed it, especially the final stop at the ice-cream store. Bob was making real progress and had several exercise sessions during the week. His soreness had gone and he was now allowing time to gradually get back into shape.

By four, Tuesday afternoon, Bob was home and ready for the planned bike ride with Sue. "I'm really quite tired today," he said, as they began the ride. "Maybe I should've come home a bit earlier for a nap."

They enjoyed a short ride and found a place for a light snack. By seven o'clock, as they were preparing to drive to the seminar, it was obvious to Sue that Bob was not as relaxed and rested as last week. In fact, he was fidgety and smoking too much. He actually looked tired and a bit depressed.

"Something wrong?" she finally asked.

"Well," said Bob, "I've been feeling really good the last few days but today I've just been dragging. I hope I can stay awake through the seminar tonight. I could fall asleep right now!"

When they arrived at the seminar, Bob said, "You go in. I'll rest here and come in just as it starts." Sue knew something was wrong but she went in and found their seats. As she arrived, she found Pam talking to Cindy and the three visited for a few minutes. Then Cindy excused herself to get ready for the session. Sue and Pam began sharing experiences and becoming better acquainted. Then Bob and Dale came in together, just as the seminar was about to begin.

"Welcome back to our third session of *Don't Eat The Soup As Hot As They Cook It!* I hope you've had a good week. We have two very important topics for tonight as we make sure the soup is nutritious, with no poison in it. Yes, we are going to talk about nutrition and deep-seated stress.

"Before we take some questions and share experiences, a friend faxed me something this week that I think you'll enjoy. I think he found it on the Internet." Everyone's attention was on the screen as Cindy read a collection of quotes taken from actual accident reports to insurance companies:

- **The pedestrian had no idea which direction to go, so I ran over him.**

- **A truck backed through my windshield and into my wife's face.**

- **I had been driving my car for forty years when I fell asleep at the wheel and had an accident.**

- **I pulled away from the side of the road, glanced at my mother-in-law and headed over the embankment.**

- **I was on my way to the doctor with rear end trouble when my universal joint gave way causing me to have an accident.**

- **The guy was all over the road; I had to swerve a number of times before I hit him.**

- **The telephone pole was approaching fast. I was attempting to swerve out of its path, when it struck my front end.**

Everyone enjoyed the humour, especially Bob. Sue noticed that Bob looked better, although it was obvious that he was not himself. Cindy answered a number of questions and then commented, "Some of you who have not been handling your stress well, but are beginning to make changes—like getting more exercise and learning to relax—will find that your emotions will vary. Some days, you'll be feeling great and other days you'll wonder if you are making any progress. Remember, it has taken months, even years, to get this run down. Give yourself time and just keep learning and doing the things you need to do to recover."

Bob looked over at Sue and said, "I guess I'm having a down day. You stay alert because I'm not sure I'll absorb much tonight. Except maybe the jokes."

"Let's move right into our first topic for tonight," Cindy began. "Someone has put it this way: *Food has always been important to me, perhaps because I started eating at such a very early age.* Dr. Peter Hanson in *The Joy of Stress* says, 'Seldom has so much been written about so little as in the field of nutrition.' And so it seems. Nutrition is so vital to life and the effective management of today's stressors. Yet this subject has become very confusing because of all the conflicting nutritional information.

"Of course, we can only touch on this important subject tonight. Our particular interest will be as it relates to stress. We do, however, offer a number of nutrition and cooking classes. Check our schedule and if you need more help in this area, talk to one of our staff or sign up for one of those classes."

Sue had already decided that one of the nutrition classes was their next priority and was quite sure Bob would come along. "Maybe some of the older kids might come. They need to learn this material now." She was drawn back to the class as a statement flashed on the screen:

A One-Sentence University Course in Nutrition

Eat at the proper times, a variety of natural foods in quantities to maintain ideal weight.

Dr. John Scharffenberg, Professor of Nutrition, Loma Linda University

"This is one of the most concise and information-packed statements on nutrition I have read. In a nutshell, it covers the whole spectrum of good eating habits." She read the statement again for emphasis.

"**Eat at the proper times**. What *are* the proper times? Two, or at most, three regular times a day, with at least five to six hours in between, for proper digestion, with no snacking. A good rule is to eat breakfast like a king, lunch like a prince, and supper like a pauper. I know someone is thinking 'What about grazing, or eating several small meals during the day? This may apply to a few medical conditions and to people with higher metabolic rates, who need several smaller meals a day, but as a general rule this is not a good habit. The body generally needs from 5–6 hours for proper digestion to take place, and eating more often simply increases the workload and requires more energy.

"**Eat a variety of natural foods**, the statement continues; that is, eat foods as unrefined as possible. A major nutritional hazard of our high-tech society is highly-processed foods. With some highly-refined breakfast cereals, the packaging is about as nutritious as the food inside. For the best nutrition, get back as close as possible to food as it's grown. Eat lots of fresh fruit and veggies, and limit or avoid the highly-processed varieties.

"**Eat quantities to maintain ideal weight**. Eat enough calories for energy but not more than is necessary. No snacking. Remember, *bigger snacks, bigger slacks!* For those needing to lose a few pounds, just cutting out snacks, especially before going to bed, and eating only at regular meal times is a major step in managing the weight problem.

"By the way, here's how you know it's time to deal with your weight problem. Step on a weigh scale and, if the message reads *One at a time please!* maybe the time has come. Or simpler yet, undress in front of a mirror and, if you look fat, you probably need to lose a few pounds.

"Dr. Scharffenberg's simple statement is based on the most up-to-date nutritional science. It also agrees with some of the best of ancient wisdom on nutrition.

"About 1000 BC, it was King Solomon who said, '…Eat at the proper times for strength and not for drunkenness.'

"Moses, quoting the Creator, and speaking of an optimum diet, said, '. . . Every seed-bearing plant on the face of the whole earth and every tree that has fruit with seed in it. They will be yours for food.'"

At this point Cindy stopped, as several people made comments and asked questions. Bob was unable to wait for the break and whispered to Sue, "I'll be back in a few minutes. I'm having a terrible time concentrating tonight. I need some air and a smoke."

"In your workbooks find the section entitled *Seven Key Nutritional Principles for Managing Stress and Maximizing Energy and Endurance*," Cindy continued. "Good nutrition is vital to managing your stress. You can relax, laugh, get exercise, and do a number of good things, but without the best of fuel, you are still going to have trouble developing the necessary positive stress hardiness. We'll take these one at a time.

"1. **Eat simple, plant-based food**, including a good variety of raw fruits and veggies, grains, and nuts in as natural a form as possible, including a portion raw. Except for the nuts, they are all low fat and high fiber. Speaking of nuts, there is some interesting research now showing the benefits of the fat in nuts, eaten in moderation of course. Generally, fats found naturally in plant-based foods are good fats and are present in proper quantities for optimum nutrition. Yes, regardless of all the hype to the contrary, it is true that plant-based food is better for optimum health than animal-based food. Research is over-whelming that a vegetarian diet is safe, adequate, and preferable to a high-fat, low-fiber and highly-processed meat diet. As a stress management tool, a more simple, natural diet is better. It contains more of the basic essential nutrients while being easier to digest and higher in energy.

"One caution here is important. When deciding to change from a meat-based diet to a plant-based diet, be prepared for some body changes. As the body adjusts to a less-stimulating, lower-fat diet, sometimes there is a temporary let-down feeling, with a frequent sense of hunger. Also, all the new tastes can sometimes cause a minor shock to the system as it adjusts, and the extra fiber loosens up the bowels. These adjustments are very mild and extremely positive. Just be patient and you will find more enjoyment in your food and a much better capacity to manage stress. For most people, a gradual change over a few weeks is easier than a quick, all-at-once change. Remember also to be tolerant of others, especially those of your family, because they may not be ready for such a drastic change in their diet.

"2. **Eat a maximum of 2 to 3 adequate, enjoyable, and unhurried meals daily**. Limit food variety to 3 or 4 kinds of food per meal and chew the food well. Enjoying your meal is very important to overall good health. Meal times should not be stressful, and eating on the run is never healthy. Digestion begins in the mouth, so taking the time to enjoy and chew your food well is very important for proper digestion. Not eating too great a variety of foods at a meal is also a good habit to follow. The body can handle about 3 or 4 different kinds quite easily."

At this point Bob returned. He had been listening while standing at the back. Turning to Sue, he said, "Sounds to me like we need that nutrition class. What would we have on our plate if we didn't have meat?" Sue nodded in agreement as Cindy continued.

"3. **Drink lots of water**. We need 6–8 glasses of water per day between our meals. It is best to drink only water between meals and not to drink much with our meals. Drink adequately between meals, eat lots of fresh fruits and vegetables, and avoid highly-spiced foods. This is much easier than you may think.

"Another good water habit is to drink a glass or two of room temperature water as soon as you get up in the morning. This flushes and cleanses the body system and prepares one for a good breakfast. Some practice and adjustments will be needed here. But don't go home and try this first thing tomorrow morning because the two glasses may just come back up C.O.D. Move gently and gradually into this positive change.

"4. **Avoid snacking**. If a snack is needed, eat some fresh fruit. Snacking is not only a problem with getting extra, unnecessary calories that increase weight, but snacking also puts additional stress on the entire body because it complicates the digestive process. For instance, it takes the body from 5–6 hours to digest the average meal. If, halfway through this process, say mid-morning, the individual eats a handful of peanuts or a donut, then the digestive process is interrupted and has to slow down to bring the new food to the digestive level of the original foods. This requires additional energy and puts an additional, unnecessary burden on the digestive system. I know people who have only one meal a day. It begins when they wake up and ends when they fall asleep. This is not a good health habit.

"5. **Keep dietary fat below 20% of total calories**. Fats are essential to good health, but one of the major challenges of current nutrition is that we are eating far too much fat. The average North American eats up to or over 40% of total calories as pure fat. We need to keep total fat calories under 20% for optimum health. Read food labels very carefully, and learn how to determine the fat-content of food. Doing this could save your life, because too much fat in the diet is the leading cause of all the major lifestyle diseases, including heart disease, cancer, and diabetes. Plant-based foods are naturally low in fat, and the fats they contain are good for you.

"6. **Use highly refined foods sparingly**, including meat, sugar, oils, and pre-packaged, highly-processed foods. Use salt wisely. As mentioned earlier, highly-refined food is one of the major nutritional hazards of living today. Most people have not thought of meat and dairy products as refined foods. Yet the beef or dairy cattle have processed natural, green food into meat and milk products.

"Refined sugar and oils are especially dangerous and should be used sparingly, if at all. It takes a lot of natural sugar cane and corn to make these very refined products. For instance, it takes 15 ears of corn to make one tablespoon of oil. Once refined, these products have no other nutrients, and some have been radically changed in the refining process so as to make them harmful instead of helpful to the body. In addition, it is very easy to overconsume these products while neglecting more wholesome foods that have a variety of nutrients. Rather than clogging the delicate body system with these highly refined foods, choose simple, natural foods as grown. Therefore, stay alert and be very cautious with highly-refined foods. As someone mentioned to me recently, if you have to read the label or, if you cannot read the label, then it is probably not the best food!

"7. Finally, **if necessary, use a good, balanced, nutritional supplement**. We are not talking about megadoses or substituting pills for food. But, for a number of reasons, a good nutritional supplement can be very beneficial. For instance, at times of additional stress, when forced to eat on the run, when travelling and unable to get the best food, a good supplement can be helpful. There are a number of good products on the market, and you will need to do some research and even some experimenting to find the best one for you.

"One final thing, before we leave nutrition," Cindy continued. "Be aware that just a little extra food can sap your energy significantly. The process of eating and digesting food is taxing to both body and brain. In fact, much of the body's energy is used in processing food. Recent studies by Dr. Masoro, at the University of Texas, clearly demonstrate that eating sparingly increases energy, prevents disease, and actually postpones aging. Therefore, it is best not to overeat. Eat to satisfy hunger and for essential calories and nutrients. Eat sparingly of high-energy, high-nutrient, natural plant foods, and skip a meal from time to time or even fast for a day periodically. In short, *eat to live rather than live to eat.*

"It's time for a break. I'll be here if anyone has questions. There are refreshments at the back. See you in twenty minutes," Cindy concluded.

"Well, this is food for thought. This session confirms some of the major food changes we need to make." Bob was thinking out loud more than speaking to anyone in particular.

Dale, who was sitting beside him, heard his musing and replied, "You're not the only ones. We also have to make some drastic changes in what we eat. I'm not sure just how we can do it, though. Life seems to be moving so fast that even proper cooking can be a burden."

"You've got that right," Bob rejoined. "Do you ever get the feeling you've been living life dangerously and didn't know it? I mean, like living too fast, eating the wrong food, and generally neglecting the things that mean the most."

"Yes, I know what you mean," Dale said, as they stood up and moved to the back of the room for a glass of water. The two men continued their discussion as they went outside for a smoke.

Meanwhile, Sue and Pam spent the break talking and comparing family and work notes. As they were heading back to their seats, Pam surprised Sue by saying, "Could we get together sometime soon for a visit? Cindy suggested that it might be helpful for me to spend some time with you. I'm at a time in my life when I'm overwhelmed and need to make some serious decisions. But I don't know where to start. You seem to have been down the road I'm on, and appear to have your life together."

"Yes, of course," Sue said instinctively. "I'd be glad to get together with you. But I'm not sure I'm that much farther down the road. I certainly don't feel my life is all that much together. Sometimes, it's helpful just to talk to someone else and compare experiences."

PRACTICAL TIPS for Ensuring the Soup is Nutritious

- eating wisely
- eating for energy and endurance
- drinking lots of water
- keeping refined fats low
- keeping refined sugars low
- eating lots of fresh fruits
- eating lots of fresh vegetables
- eating some raw food daily
- avoiding overeating
- eating simple plant-based foods
- eating refined foods sparingly
- taking a good nutritional supplement

"About the only time I have available this week is noon on Friday," said Pam. "Is that OK for you?"

Sue did a quick mental check. "Yes, I think that's a good time. Where should we meet?" The two ladies were discussing details as Bob and Dale returned, and they all took their seats. Sue felt good about Pam opening up, and was hopeful that she could be of some help. On the other hand, she was a bit frightened about being someone who appeared to have her stress act together.

Stress Management Principles

- Pinpoint and recognize the main stress producers in your life and take appropriate action—now!

- Develop an awareness of how stress is affecting you and listen to your body's stress-warning signals.

- Learn to control the stress response by calling a time out, breathing deeply, analyzing the situation, looking for humour and cutting yourself some slack.

- Learn the relaxation response and activate it often.

- Get regular daily physical activity.

- Humour is a wonderful stress buffer. Begin immediately to create a humour survival kit and use it regularly.

- Eat a wide variety of natural, plant-based foods (including some raw) for maximum energy and endurance.

Beware Of Poison In The Soup

Resolving deep-seated stress

"**B**EWARE of poison in the soup," Cindy emphasized, as she called the class back to order. She then moved quickly into the topic, knowing she had very little time to introduce and cover this part of the seminar.

"We will now look briefly at two major areas where your stress soup can become very dangerous. The first is the use of drugs, either recreationally or as medicine, and the second is what I call deep-seated stress.

"Every drug introduced into the body has negative side effects. This does not mean we should never use drugs. There are times when the benefits far outweigh the risks. We simply need to recognize that all drugs affect the delicate balance in which our body functions and they need to be used carefully and with wisdom.

"Unfortunately, in our society, drugs are seen as miracle products and are used much too freely as a quick fix. This is especially true in stress management. It's much quicker to pop a pill than it is to exercise regularly or take the time to learn how to relax. The truth is that drugs have only a very limited benefit in long-term stress management.

"A basic life principle is to use, in moderation, what is good and helpful, and avoid all that is harmful. This means avoiding all dangerous, addictive drugs. Most of these artificial substances only complicate the stress soup. In addition, they accumulate substantial *pay-later* debts. With any drug, for the extra, temporary lift or spurt of energy, there is always the corresponding low. Addiction happens when the body gets hooked on the high and, in an attempt to avoid the low, it craves more of the drug. We are not just talking about powerful prescription or illegal drugs, but some very common everyday drugs, like caffeine, nicotine, and alcohol.

"How many people do you know who do not have at least one cup of coffee, tea, or caffeine-added cola in a day? Or maybe it's an extra-strength pain reliever. Yet, regardless of its widespread use, caffeine is an addictive and very dangerous drug!" Cindy warned.

"Because caffeine's effect appears mild, many do not see the risks. Actually, caffeine damages the body in a number of ways, including irritation of the stomach, kidneys, and a number of other organs. It also increases blood-sugar levels and interferes with calcium and iron absorption. But the worst negative effects are those on the nervous system, which becomes overstimulated by tremors, nervousness, anxiety, and sleep deficiency. Over time, these symptoms can give way to chronic fatigue, lack of energy, and persistent insomnia.

"And then there's nicotine, one of the most deadly poisons that can be introduced into the body. Who doesn't know of its deadly results? Yet it's so addictive that it's one of the most difficult habits to break. Smokers often use nicotine as a stress reliever. In reality, the opposite is true. Yes, smokers, it is a deception! Smoking does not relieve your stress. Smoking actually creates more stress on the body. The sense of relaxation you feel appears real but is simply an illusion! If you're a smoker, one of the best things you can do to help you manage your stress is to quit. Now it *is* true that the quitting process, for a few days, is for most people very stressful as the body divorces Lady Nicotine. But the benefits of quitting are well worth the effort and go far beyond stress management to include a large number of additional health benefits. So get the help you need, and just do it!"

Bob had a major stress response just thinking about quitting his twenty-year smoking habit. He'd had first-hand experience as to how negatively his body reacted when he tried to quit once before. He wasn't looking forward to a repeat of *that* experience. Yet he knew that he must try again, soon. Somehow, he had a sense that this time he would win.

First, he thought, *I need to get my stress under control. Then I'll set the date to quit—and do it!*

As he turned and his eyes met Sue's, she could sense his fear. She gave him a knowing nod and gently whispered, "We'll do it together, and we'll win!"

Cindy went on. "We don't have time tonight to discuss the dangers of alcohol, marijuana, and a host of other hard drugs, both legal and illegal, that appear to relieve stress. Alcohol is the most commonly used of all the hard drugs. Its dangers are well known, including its negative effects on the brain. It especially attacks the crucial frontal lobes, where we make all of our decisions.

"Speaker and humorist Mike Warnke, who knows first-hand the hazards of using drugs and alcohol, describes the major stress-related dangers this way: 'You get two weeks behind on your rent, so you decide, *Well, I'm behind on my rent; guess I'll get high. Maybe it will go away.* So you get strung out on dope, or alcohol, and stay that way for two weeks. When you come down, you are now four weeks behind on your rent. When you got high you didn't have any food in the icebox. When you come back down, you find out that somebody has stolen the icebox. It's a progressive deal—it just gets worse and worse. The only thing that drugs do for you is to cloud your vision so that you can't see that things are getting worse and worse. By the time you come to your senses, you're up to your neck.'

"Now that is *not* stress management." Cindy paused and looked around. "It's avoidance, which solves nothing. In summary, drugs of all kinds, simply cause the body more stress most of the time. Avoid them whenever possible. Use more natural ways of managing your stress."

Bob was listening to this section very intently. He knew smoking had to go, but coffee! Well, that was a shock and seemed a bit extreme. *For all the alcohol, I use,* he thought, *it's not a problem, and other hard drugs have never been a problem.* Recently, he'd been using sleeping pills quite frequently. He realized he would need to be careful with them.

Sue, knowing Bob so well, sensed his reaction and whispered, "What she's saying is true. I recently read some research on this. We need to find some alternative drinks that are caffeine-free. For us, the change should not be that hard. We may experience some minor withdrawal symptoms, but nothing serious."

Their attention returned to Cindy as she was saying, "The second area of potential poison in the soup is deep-seated stress. This segment of the seminar will be covered by a guest lecturer. It is my pleasure to introduce Dr. Harvey Morgan, a medical doctor, health educator, and seminar presenter who has some pastoral counselling experience. Several people in this class know him from his wellness seminar, *The Wellness Factor*. He will now lead the discussion on deep-seated stress."

After the welcoming applause, Dr. Morgan thanked Cindy for the invitation to share in the seminar, and moved right into the topic. "What do we mean by deep-seated stress? First of all, superficial stress, which is basically most of the stress that has been discussed so far, is external. It can be caused by any number of stressors, including the irritations and perplexities that result from specific pressures and situations. Deep-seated stress, on the other hand, is internal. It is a different stress that is not necessarily generated by specific stressors but by certain situations that merely expose or magnify their existence. Deep-seated stress includes low self-worth, unresolved grief, guilt, negative emotions—like anger, hostility, hatred, jealousy, and revenge—and negative attitudes—like pessimism, criticism, and cynicism—and unnatural fear and anxiety, and hopelessness and depression.

"You can readily see that deep-seated stress involves different stressors that require addressing in distinct ways. Attitude is very important in resolving deep-seated stress in our lives. Here is a little story that has been a real help to me in regards to attitude.

"Sidney Harris, writing in the *Chicago Daily News*, told the story of walking to the newsstand with a Quaker friend. The friend bought a paper and thanked the newsboy politely. The boy only grunted.

'A solemn fellow, isn't he?' Mr. Harris commented.

'Yes, he's that way every night.'

'Yet I noticed that you went out of your way to be courteous to him,' responded Mr. Harris. And his Quaker friend replied, 'Why should I let him decide how I am going to act?'

What a great illustration, thought Sue. *How often do I let others determine how I react?* She also began to realize that there were a number of deep-seated issues in their lives. Gary's death was still fresh in both their minds, and they had barely begun to deal with the grief. The anger and fear in connection with Kathy's cancer was also very real.

"We will look briefly now at each of these deep-seated stress areas," continued Dr. Morgan.

"The first is **resolving low self-worth**. Other words or related words or concepts are self-esteem, self-image, and self-respect. Self-worth refers to our value and how we relate to and value ourselves. Ancient wisdom says, *Love your neighbour as yourself*. Unless we have a healthy self-worth or self-respect, how can we be positive and caring toward others?"

At this point, Dr. Morgan asked, "What is it that makes you valuable?" After a few seconds of silence he asked, "What makes gold so valuable?" Almost immediately, someone spoke up, "Because it's so rare."

"Exactly," Morgan said. "And here's the good news. When they made you, they threw away the mould! I know that in a group of this size someone is thinking, *It's a good thing because the world cannot take two of me*." A chuckle rippled across the audience as the doctor continued. "It really is a good thing, because it makes you very rare and very special. Actually, you *are* one of a kind, not only on this planet but also in the entire universe. Therefore, you are very valuable and very precious. To reap the benefits of this truth, you must accept your intrinsic value and enjoy and apply it in your life. For those of us who grew up with a low sense of our worth, this will take some effort and a change in attitude toward ourselves."

At this point, Dr. Morgan became very serious and said, "During this seminar, you have discussed physical health principles extensively, and some mental ones too, but until now you have not considered the spiritual. We are total beings—physically, mentally, emotionally, and spiritually. In our western culture, we have actually tried to separate these and, as a result, many people are very uncomfortable discussing either the emotional or spiritual side of their lives. These important aspects of our lives are only minimally considered, or ignored altogether. This is very unfortunate, and a major cause of much deep-seated stress. Emotional concerns are getting more attention today but the spiritual, while getting some attention, is still largely sidelined.

"I can understand the reluctance of many to deal with this area of their lives because of the large number of confusing ideas in the religious world. *Religion* or *religious* doesn't necessarily mean *spiritual*. I've done considerable research into all the major world religions and have found my spiritual peace in a personal relationship with the amazing God of the Bible.

"I realize that even in the Jewish and Christian religious worlds from which the Bible comes, there is much spiritual confusion. However, when you read the Bible itself, honestly seeking truth and asking for spiritual guidance from the Creator God, it is simply amazing how simple, clear, and reasonable the message is. Should you have any interest in pursuing this spiritual route, simply get a good contemporary translation of the Bible and begin reading in the New Testament on the life of Jesus Christ. You will be amazed as to how your heart will be strangely warmed as you discover an extremely caring and personal man who not only demonstrated that he was more than a man but was also the mighty Creator God. The many amazing miracles of healing, his untimely death in his early thirties, and then the marvelous story of his resurrection, will inspire and encourage you.

"Well, enough of that for now. Somehow, when dealing with deep-seated stress, I get off on that spiritual tangent," said Dr. Morgan, realizing that he had become sidetracked. Then he added, "I guess I get a little carried away here because my spiritual experience means so much to me personally and also because, in resolving deep-seated stress, the spiritual component is so important. In improving low self-worth, the idea of a personal, caring God, as Creator, is a major asset and adds considerable value to life. The spiritual component is also especially helpful in dealing with grief.

"On that note, let us move on to **resolving and recovering from grief**." As Dr. Morgan began to make the transition, Sue noticed Bob fidgeting. *His self-worth*, she thought, *has taken a real beating over the last several months. He has always been so strong, decisive, and confident, but now it seems as if life is a burden.* She also recognized that neither of them were particularly religious and she wondered about his reaction to the spiritual input.

While Dr. Morgan handled a few questions on self-worth and on his spiritual remarks, Bob whispered to Sue, "First time I ever heard a medical doctor talk about religion in a positive light. Maybe we should check it out sometime. Did you know that Jim and Kathy have just recently started attending a church near where we live? It seems to be helping them in their time of need."

Sue, a bit surprised at Bob's positive reaction, just nodded and refocused on the speaker as he said, "Grief can be a major stressor. Grief is caused not only by the death of a loved one but by any loss. For example, the loss of a job, or a home, or even an expectation can result in grief at some level. I have counselled people who have been in a state of grief for years and have not yet begun the grief-recovery process. Some can actually become physically and mentally ill because they have not resolved their grief.

"One lady that I counselled a few years ago was physically ill. She had a number of serious physical symptoms: headaches, chronic upset stomach, as well as a number of flu-like symptoms, and had been dragging herself around the house. Her physicians could find nothing physically wrong. After visiting with her, I discovered that she had lost her husband in a serious car accident two years before and, because the body was so smashed up, the casket could not be opened at the funeral. It eventually became clear to me, from our discussions, that she was still expecting him to return home some day soon. She had not yet started the grief process and had not even accepted the fact that her husband was dead.

"I had to be very direct with her. I told her that her husband was not coming back, that he was indeed dead, and that she needed to accept that fact. She became very upset with me but, within a couple of days, she was physically well. She had finally accepted the fact that her husband was not going to return. At that point, after two years, she was just starting the grieving process. Her physical symptoms disappeared almost overnight. Unresolved grief can become a source of significant stress. If you find yourself needing help with this stressor, seek help and move on.

"Recovering from grief begins with acceptance. The guidelines on the screen will help with the process:"

1. **Allow yourself to grieve.** Remember, grief is not the problem; it's the solution. Just as surgery requires time to recover, so does any trauma. Becoming impatient only compounds stress.

2. **Invest yourself again.** Look for people and situations in which you can invest your love and energy.

3. **Let your faith mature.** Loss reminds us of life's impermanence. Every grief experience invites you to reaffirm your faith and hope.

4. **Lean on others.** Share your grief with others. It's been well said, "Friends divide grief and multiply joys. Sometimes you can't do it alone. You don't have to!"

"A final note on grief," continued Dr. Morgan. "Even when it is resolved, the loss will always be there, but the pain is gone, or at least significantly diminished. Enjoying the positive memories of a lost loved one can be a healthy sign of grief recovery.

"**Resolving guilt** is number three," continued Morgan, without allowing time for questions. "Some experts will tell you that all guilt is bad when, in fact, there is both good and bad guilt. What is good guilt? It is guilt that comes from doing something that is wrong according to your accepted value system. For example, you become angry and say something unkind and hurtful to a friend or co-worker and you sense something is not right. This guilt is good in the sense that it is a warning mechanism to tell you that you are off track.

"What is bad guilt?" he continued. After a short pause, he said, "It is guilt that is not yours. Many people today take on guilt that is not theirs. For example, a parent may experience guilt because of the negative actions of an adult child. There is an abundant supply of other people's guilt that you can take on if you wish. Some people seem to be more prone to taking on others' guilt and it causes them enormous unnecessary stress.

"How do you resolve good guilt?" Morgan asked.

Someone immediately spoke up and said, "Confess your mistake and make it right."

"Excellent," said the instructor. "When you've said something that has hurt someone, you ask their forgiveness and restore the relationship. What about bad guilt? How does a person get rid of *it*?"

Again someone spoke up, "Give it back to whomever it belongs and leave it there."

"Excellent," replied Morgan. "Again, if you need help dealing with guilt, either bad or good, seek help and you will be resolving a major life stressor.

"Number four is **resolving negative emotions**—like anger, hostility, hatred, jealousy, and revenge." Morgan moved on quickly. "Emotions are merely reactions. You feel how you feel, be that anger or love. These feelings are neither good nor bad. Even with what may be called negative emotions, there are times when, at least temporarily, you will experience them. For example, we *should* be angry when we witness injustice or racism. However, to harbour anger, hostility, hatred, jealousy and revenge, and to dwell on them, is very damaging and, if left unresolved, can seriously undermine our physical and mental health.

"Forgiveness, tolerance, and a positive, caring attitude for people, even for those we do not understand, or maybe don't like, is the best antidote for negative emotions. There are also times when we have to forgive someone who has severely hurt us and who will never ask for our forgiveness. They may or may not have any understanding of how they hurt us, but refusing to forgive them and move on, hurts only ourselves. An example is in the case of some forms of abuse. The abuser may never realize or accept, even after punishment, the pain and hurt he/she has caused. For the victim not to forgive and instead cherish hatred, hurts only the victim not the abuser. Again, professional help may be needed to fully resolve these stressors.

"**Resolving negative attitudes**—like pessimism, criticism, and cynicism—is our fifth group of deep-seated stressors," Dr. Morgan continued. "These negative attitudes can be fatal to the enjoyment of life. The antidote is optimism and positive thinking. Hardening of the attitudes is just as deadly as hardening of the arteries! Notice here, on the screen, five keys to developing positive attitudes."

1. Accept people as they are; accept situations that cannot be changed.

2. Be adaptable to people, situations, and change.

3. Appreciate what you have and where you are right now!

4. Act positively with focus; take one step at a time.

5. Have realistic expectations.

"Chronic negative attitudes in a normally positive and upbeat person, can be a major sign of the advanced stages of burnout," Dr. Morgan emphasized. "In the advanced stages of burnout, which we will discuss at our last session, even a very positive person can become very cynical, critical, or pessimistic. In this case, recovery from the burnout is the first step.

"Number six in managing deep-seated stress is **resolving unnatural fear and anxiety**. Some people are more prone to anxiety than others. We are talking here of unnatural fear. Fear, in itself, is not bad. In fact, there are things we need to fear. We are talking here of that paralyzing fear that grips some individuals and limits their ability to function.

"Everyone experiences fear at some time but generally our two greatest fears are fear of the unknown and fear of being alone. Healthy fear is realistic and keeps us alert and warns us of dangers. Neurotic anxiety is a type of fear that results from distorted thoughts with little or no basis in reality. This anxiety is inappropriate and unhealthy, and leads to worry about things that never happen. It makes us unproductive and focused on *What if...* . The major antidotes for fear are trust and knowledge.

"Finally," said Dr. Morgan, "number seven: **resolving hopelessness and depression**. The feeling and sense of hopelessness is very dangerous. The antidote is hope—the realization that all life has a worthwhile purpose. Hope shows us that there is more to life than what meets the eye.

"Depression can range all the way from feeling blue to feeling that life is meaningless. When you're feeling down, these steps may help:

1. **Extend yourself and talk to someone.**

2. **Ask yourself why you feel sad or down. Can you do anything to change your mood? Challenge yourself. Ask if it is realistic to look at the situation differently.**

3. **Begin something new and/or good for yourself or someone else.**

"I read recently of a seventy-four-year-old lady who felt so down and depressed that she was ready to die. Life had lost all meaning and she felt worn out and useless. Somehow, she got involved in a seniors' project and before long had a new lease on life, with purpose and new goals. At age ninety-one, she wrote her first book and started travelling and promoting an environmental issue for seniors.

"This is a very brief introduction to deep-seated stress," concluded Dr. Morgan. After answering a number of questions, he turned the seminar back to Cindy, who thanked him and, after another round of applause she said, "Dr. Morgan will return for our last session and lead our discussion on burnout. Don't miss that session, as it will explain clearly why many of you are having such severe stress signals.

"We will spend the remainder of our time tonight in our groups. Again, we want to give you an opportunity to act on the information you have learned tonight by sharing it with those in your group.

"Turn to this page in your workbook." She flashed the following page on the screen:

Improving The Recipe For A Better Soup

My Action Plan For This Week

- **Start:** _____

- **Stop:** _____

- **Keep:** _____

"Tonight, we have discussed nutrition and deep-seated stress. It is again decision time! By the way, how many of you made some progress over the last week?" Hands went up all over the auditorium and Cindy continued. "Just like last week, write in the blank beside *Start*, one thing that you are going to start doing immediately to manage your stress better. Then, beside *Stop*, write one thing you are going to immediately stop doing because it is not helping you manage your stress. Finally, because we have all survived and are doing some things right, beside *Keep,* write something that you are going to keep doing because it has been helping you manage your stress effectively. You have a few minutes to do this exercise."

Sue had already written the answers on her page. She was going to *Start* focusing more clearly on her family's diet. *Nutrition is definitely going to improve in the Picco home!* she thought. She decided to *Stop* letting others control the way she reacted to negative things. She would be nice to others, even if they were having a bad day and showing it. Beside *Keep*, Sue wrote, continue with my exercise program.

Bob was studying his page very carefully as Sue completed hers and glanced over at his. Beside *Start*, she saw him write *explore the spiritual*. Surprised, she said, "Are you sure?"

"Yes," whispered Bob. "This may help with some of the other changes we need to make." Beside *Stop*, he wrote *stop smoking*. "No, I am not going to stop smoking tonight or even this week," he said, "but the decision has been made and when that next stop-smoking seminar comes along, I'm going to set the date and quit."

"Okay," said Cindy. "Let's break into our groups. If possible, please stay with the same group. As you get to know each other better you will develop a mutual support system. Once you are together, share a joke or two and then discuss what you wrote in the decision exercise. We have about the same amount of time as last week."

Bob and Sue arranged their chairs so they were facing Dale and Pam. Sue had been looking forward to this part of the seminar as a time to get better acquainted with Pam and her husband. Bob was obviously still having a difficult evening and it was not until Dale told a joke that he seemed to return to his normal self. All four seemed to enjoy the discussion and it was a good time to get to know each other better. Bob even opened up a little and shared his feelings about Gary's recent death. Their discussion of deep-seated stress was very meaningful.

It seemed like only minutes had passed when Cindy announced that time was up. She then reminded everyone of next week's topics and dismissed the group. Bob said to Sue, "Let's go quickly. I'm not feeling very well, so would you drive?" As they were leaving, Pam said, "See you on Friday, Sue, and after tonight we'll *have* to have a healthy lunch!"

PRACTICAL TIPS for Getting Rid of Poison in the Soup

- resolving deep-seated stress
- avoiding addictive drugs
- being aware of "quick fixes"
- talking and sharing your feelings
- forgiving freely
- working off your anger
- letting go of "what if's"
- crying it out
- stopping smoking
- encouraging someone
- resolving guilt
- ignoring rumours
- reconciling where possible
- talk it out with family and co-workers
- being empathic, not overly sensitive
- eliminating destructive self-talk
- being clear on what is expected of you
- accepting loss and dealing with grief
- developing positive relationships
- terminating toxic relationships
- writing down the pain and ripping it up
- refusing to live in the past
- volunteering/helping someone
- expecting the unexpected
- valuing yourself
- dealing with low self-worth

"Good!" Sue replied. "See you then; I'm looking forward to it."

The drive home was quiet. Bob went straight to bed, which was unusual for him. Sue visited with the children and reviewed plans for

the rest of the week. She was looking forward to her bike ride with
Cindy in the morning, as she had a number of questions.

Stress Management Principles

- Pinpoint and recognize the main stress producers in your life and take appropriate action—now!

- Develop an awareness of how stress is affecting you and listen to your body's stress-warning signals.

- Learn to control the stress response by calling a time out, breathing deeply, analyzing the situation, looking for humour and cutting yourself some slack.

- Learn the relaxation response and activate it often.

- Get regular daily physical activity.

- Humour is a wonderful stress buffer. Begin immediately to create a humour survival kit and use it regularly.

- Eat a wide variety of natural, plant-based foods (including some raw) for maximum energy and endurance.

- Avoid addictive drugs and resolve deep-seated stressors, such as low self-worth, grief, guilt, negative emotions, negative attitudes, unnatural anxiety and hopelessness.

9

Give Thanks For The Soup

Developing the "attitude of gratitude"

Bob Picco had a restless night. He had fallen asleep quickly but woke up when Sue came to bed and did not sleep well all night. By morning, he was exhausted and stayed in bed. When he didn't show up for breakfast, Sue became concerned and decided it was time to check out the problem. She found him still in bed, half awake, and asked how he was feeling.

"Totally exhausted, and my stomach has been upset all night," he said. "I haven't felt this bad in months. I'm taking the day off. Would you call the office and tell Jim I'll give him a call later."

After calling the office, Sue checked Bob's temperature. It was a bit high but nothing serious. *This is strange*, she thought. *He hasn't missed a day at work for months. He's been tired and exhausted but always able to function.* She decided to just leave him alone for the morning and, if he wasn't feeling better by lunch, she would call the doctor. As she was getting ready to meet Cindy about mid-morning, Sue stopped by the bedroom and found him sound asleep.

The bike ride with Cindy was refreshing, both physically and mentally. Their friendship was developing nicely and they were mutually supportive. They discovered a number of areas where they were kindred spirits, and sensed that their friendship would last. As she was leaving for home after the ride, Sue casually mentioned that she needed to check on her patient.

"What patient?" asked Cindy.

"Bob," she answered. "He was very tired yesterday and last night at the seminar, and didn't go to work today. He was asleep when I left—hope he's feeling better now."

"Bob didn't look very alert last night," Cindy said. "He wasn't his usual chipper self."

"He hasn't been himself for some time, except once in a while," Sue explained. "But for him to miss a day at the office, he must be ill." After telling Cindy about her upcoming visit with Pam, Sue headed home and found Bob up and feeling much better.

"After I threw up last night's supper, my stomach has gradually been feeling better," reported Bob.

"Sounds like mild food poisoning," said Sue. "What have you eaten that the rest of us haven't? After reviewing their meals they concluded that the only possible cause would have been the chicken he had eaten just before the seminar. Sue had been cutting back on meats and had chosen not to order the chicken, but Bob had.

"You know," said Bob, "it was shortly after we ate supper last night that my stomach felt funny. Being tired all day, I just assumed I was coming down with some virus. I'm sure it was that chicken. Now I'm feeling better and I may drop by the office later. No, on second thought, I'm going to take the whole day off and maybe read a book or something."

Sue agreed. "That's a good idea! I was reading a magazine article recently about the dangers of eating meat. It's extremely high in fat and cholesterol, which we hear so much about in the media. There are a number of serious diseases that are traced to various meats, and a high protein diet has been demonstrated to shorten our life span. As Cindy mentioned last night, we should eat meat sparingly, if at all."

"This could be a turning point for me," said Bob. "I seem to be getting a number of signals to cut back or cut out meat. I've been eating more fresh fruits and vegetables and enjoying them. The upcoming class on nutrition should be helpful."

The next morning Bob felt fine. Actually, he was feeling good because not only had he managed a good night's sleep, but relaxing the previous afternoon and evening had allowed time enough for some additional exercise and a nap. He actually got very little reading done.

Before Sue knew it, Friday had arrived and she was on her way for the lunch appointment with Pam. She was looking forward to getting to know Pam better, yet feeling a degree of apprehension. How was she going to be of help to someone she barely knew? *I'll just have to wing it, and see what happens*, she thought.

Pam seemed more relaxed, Sue noticed, as they met and ordered their lunch. "After the seminar on Tuesday, I decided to see my doctor," Pam announced. "I've been extremely tired for weeks and I've become more and more angry and frustrated. Well, the doctor gave me a couple of weeks of sick leave and said it looks like most of my symptoms are stress related. I am so glad we can visit. My female support system is quite limited right now. Just to visit and talk will be helpful."

Sue relaxed immediately because she could see that Pam had recognized part of the problem and was beginning to get help. Being Pam's friend, Sue knew she could manage, but beyond that she was very uncomfortable. As they visited, Pam told Sue about all of her activities. Sue was amazed that anyone would attempt so much, especially with a young family.

Finally, as Pam began to wind down, Sue got a chance to speak. "Pam, no wonder you're tired. You're trying to be superwoman. You may have overextended yourself. It's obvious that you are a high-energy person, but no one can keep up that pace without burning out. Have you thought through a relaxing plan for the next two weeks?"

"Maybe you can help me with that," Pam said hopefully.

Sue answered almost instinctively. "It seems you simply need to slow down and do things you really enjoy. What are the three things that you would do if you had all day?"

Pam thought for a moment, then she said, "I need to spend more time with Dale and the kids."

"Need to or want to?" asked Sue.

"Both," Pam replied. "I really enjoy family time but it seems, lately, that I have no time, and when we do, my mind is somewhere else. Have you ever felt that way?"

"Oh yes, I've been there, done that!" said Sue. "In fact, it is only since I quit working full time that life has been relatively manageable for me. Even now, there are times when life gets moving too fast and I feel out of control. What else is on the top of your relaxation list?"

"Sleep and shopping," Pam said, almost without thinking.

"There you have it. During the next two weeks, get extra sleep, do some leisurely shopping—window shopping if you like—and plan some special, but simple family times. Enjoy your kids and husband, give yourself permission to relax and do it! Does it sound possible?"

Pam was quiet for a while before she answered. "Yes, it is possible but it will require some major adjustments. The stress management seminar has made this very clear and, I guess, now is the time for action. Oh my!" Pam looked at her watch. "I forgot all about the time. I have an important city council meeting in ten minutes." Then, catching herself, she said, "No. What if I don't go today? Actually the doctor did say to take the next two weeks off."

Pam reached into her handbag and took out her cell phone. She called her secretary and cancelled all her afternoon appointments. Then she said, "I'm going home for a quick nap before the kids get home from school. When they get home, I'll take them to the park and, when Dale gets home, we'll all go out for supper and then decide on something fun for the evening. Sometime over the weekend, I'll plan next week. How's that for a start, Sue?"

"Excellent! I think you're on the right track. Just remember to take your time, pace yourself, and you'll be your old self before you know it."

"Thanks for listening and helping me focus," Pam said, before the two ladies went their separate ways. "See you at the seminar on Tuesday."

Sue felt good as she drove home. *That wasn't nearly as difficult as it could have been,* she thought. *Both Pam and Bob are going to make it, and get their stress under control, because they recognize the problem and are beginning to do something about it.*

The weekend went by quickly. Bob was now beginning to get the hang of the relaxation thing and got some needed rest. The family actually managed both a hike at the nearby national park and a three-hour bike ride along the old railway tracks near their house. Everyone, including the teenagers, appeared to have a good time.

The family even had a discussion about Gary's death, their first since the funeral. Both Sue and Bob were amazed at how it had affected the children. They needed to go through the grief process too. Their fears centred on the possibility of losing their parents in a similar event. Bob, for the first time, shared his real feelings about the loss and how it had affected both him and their business. Death had become a sinister and unwelcome intruder for the first time, and they were just beginning to come to grips with it.

Suddenly, Sue thought of Gary's wife, Caroline. "We should invite her and the children over for a meal sometime soon. It's nearly six weeks since Gary died and she probably needs additional support right now."

"Good idea," said Bob. "You kids can plan some entertainment for her children and give her a break." All four children were excited about the idea and began making plans. Sue would drop by and visit Caroline early in the week to see how she was doing, and to set a date. The entire discussion was a step in the process of resolving the deep-seated stressor of grief that had been hanging over the Picco family for weeks.

The next two days slipped by without incident. Just before the seminar on Tuesday, while they were having their evening meal out, Sue told Bob about her visit with Caroline earlier in the day. "She was really glad to see me. It seems that since the funeral she hasn't had many visitors and was feeling quite lonely. With two preschoolers, I think she just enjoyed talking to an adult for a change, and I could relate to that. Our plan to invite them over, which, by the way, has evolved from a meal to an all-day event—the kids' idea—got her very excited. We scheduled it for this Sunday. I hope you don't have other plans."

"No," said Bob. "It sounds like as good a time as any. We just need to plan it and do it."

They got to the seminar just as Cindy was welcoming everyone. Pam and Dale were already seated and Sue noticed that Pam was looking a bit more relaxed than she had on Friday. She just *had* to whisper to her, "You're looking great, Pam. Is it the extra sleep, or shopping?"

"It's the sleep," Pam said quietly. "I slept just about all weekend. Shopping will have to wait until I get caught up on my rest."

Cindy had finished the introduction and was taking some questions. Someone was asking, "Why is it that as I relax, all I can do is sleep? How long will this last? Is it normal?"

"Yes, it *is* normal and the reason is that you have most likely been overextended and the body is simply rebuilding. Rest is an excellent stress buffer and it is during sleep that the body restores itself. How long it will last varies from person to person. For some, only a couple of weekends of extra rest will do it. For others, it may take a few months. It depends on the degree of exhaustion. Extra physical exercise will also help hasten the process. I know that it seems strange to exercise when you're tired, but it will shorten the recovery time by improving your blood circulation. Give yourself time. Remember, you didn't get to this state overnight and the recovery will take time."

It took thirty to forty minutes for Cindy to answer all the questions because the group had bonded by now and was relaxed and comfortable asking questions and making comments. Everyone appreciated the question time because most had similar questions that needed answering.

"Okay," said Cindy. "You're asking excellent questions, and most of you are making great progress in managing your stress more effectively. We're getting our stress soup cooled off, right? How many of you feel that you've made significant progress over the last three weeks?" Hands went up all across the auditorium.

"That's great," Cindy said, as she moved into her topic. "Tonight we'll look at the last two of our eight major stress management principles. They are *Give Thanks For The Soup* and *Eat The Soup Slowly And Enjoy It*!"

"Our first principle, giving thanks for the soup, is developing an *attitude of gratitude*. Recognize that life is a precious gift from the Creator and is lived best with optimism and thankfulness. Combine gratefulness with unselfish caring and sensitivity for others, and you have a truly winning combination.

"Recognizing the privilege of life, and being thankful for being alive, goes a long way in offsetting the challenges of life. I've been working with people long enough to know that everyone has their difficult times, but everyone also has their blessings. Look for and enjoy the positive while accepting the challenges in stride. Sometimes, this means accepting what you cannot change and simply moving on. The well-known serenity prayer fits in so well at this point. Let's read it aloud together." The group began to read from the screen:

> God grant me the serenity
> To accept the things I cannot change,
> The courage to change the things I can,
> And the wisdom to know the difference.

"Here's how a couple of ancient writers encourage thankfulness:

> O give thanks to the Lord, for He is good, and His love for us never ends.
> — King David, Psalm 118:1

> Always be joyful. Always have a prayerful attitude. In every situation be thankful to God for what He has done for you.
> — The Apostle Paul, Thessalonians 5:16 – 18
> (both excerpts from The Clear Word)

"Now, in your workbook, write a few of the things for which you are thankful," Cindy continued. "Those who haven't done this type of exercise for a while, or who may be feeling down and hurting, may have to think this through very deliberately and carefully, but it is an excellent daily exercise to help keep life in proper focus."

Today I Am Thankful For

1. _____

2. _____

3. _____

4. _____

5. _____

Both Bob and Sue had already taken some time thinking through the positives in their lives and found this exercise very easy and enjoyable. Bob whispered to Sue just as she finished, "A couple of weeks ago, I would have had a hard time with this exercise, but this seminar has really helped me focus on priorities. I am beginning to feel more positive and in control. Thanks for getting me to that wellness seminar."

Sue was about to respond when Cindy asked the group to share some of the things for which they were thankful. Immediately, hands went up across the room. People responded with a variety of things— general things like good health, family, friends, good food, freedom, and more specific things, like healing from a serious illness, a caring spouse, a pet, et cetera.

Bob spoke up and said, "I'm especially thankful for the timing of this seminar, with its excellent material that Sue and I have needed for quite some time, but did not realize it. You've done a great job, Cindy! Thanks!"

Immediately the room broke out in applause. It was obvious that most participants had received benefits and were very thankful. Bob and Cindy were taken off guard by the response but both joined in wholeheartedly.

Cindy appreciated and enjoyed the thank you. "You're a great class," she said. "Most of you are making great progress. Just keep up the good work and the daily joy of stress will be a reality.

"Now, to our second principle of giving thanks for the soup—developing and enjoying your spirituality. Some researchers are calling this the surprise key to stress management.

"It is important for each of us to recognize, and accept the fact, that we are whole persons, physically, mentally, emotionally and, yes, spiritually. As Dr. Morgan mentioned last week, Western society has, somehow, separated these basic components and has almost totally ignored our spiritual side. Generally, the practice of medicine, instead of treating persons as total beings, has developed a system of medical doctors for physical illnesses, psychologists and psychiatrists for mental and emotional problems, but has almost totally avoided the spiritual in actual practice. The spiritual has been left to organized religion, with the general idea that religion is not scientific and therefore less important. Recently, Dr. Herbert Benson of Harvard University, and a number of others, have conducted some interesting studies on the importance of faith and prayer, with some very positive results. Because the approach is more scientific, and results can be measured to a degree, their research is getting some attention.

"Dr. Benson refers to what he calls *the faith factor*. There is now significant evidence that people who believe in God as a loving and caring heavenly parent, and who actively cultivate that faith relationship, have one of the most effective tools for managing stress in a crisis and achieving long-term health.

"A number of others, including Dr. George Sheehan, a cardiologist and the *grandfather* of modern jogging for fitness, credits the connection to a higher power with alleviating the stressors of uncertainty and insecurity, and providing an inner sense of calm and tranquility, even in the midst of crisis and upheaval. The sense that no defeat is final, and that each day provides new opportunities and hope, is grounded in a firm belief in God.

"Today, it appears that spirituality is in, but organized religion is out. Interest in our spiritual side has always been important. For some people, it has been a major part of their overall life plan. Yet spirituality has been, and remains, a confusing or neglected side for many people. For me, I come from the Christian perspective and believe in a personal God who created us, and loves and watches over all creation. The Bible, for me, is God's love letter to His creation, and is full of guidance and instruction for living a successful and meaningful life. But what does all this have to do with managing stress? Simply this—for many people, one of their major stress buffers and key coping skills, is their spiritual experience with God. A personal relationship, which includes regular prayer, Bible study, and community fellowship with a group of caring, like-minded believers, is a regular and positive part of their life.

"We cannot explore spirituality in depth in this short seminar, but I do want to plant some seed thoughts in this area which you can explore more fully later. Regardless of where you come from spiritually, consider the spiritual side of your experience and develop it. You will find it a major strength in effectively managing your stress. Some of you may have had negative experiences with organized religion. Process those hurts, but don't let the bad experience destroy what can become a major tool for peace in your life.

"One caution." Cindy raised her hand. "Spirituality is not some mystical and magical power, or unreal essence. It is not some superstitious power that works good, or bad, depending on what we do or don't do. The spiritual is equally as real as the physical. It is a relationship with a real person, the Creator God. For Christians, this person is Jesus Christ, who is the Creator and who became a man, and lived among us to reveal the truth about God and spirituality. Jesus taught the dignity of both men and women, and demonstrated a love of people and life that still stands today, 2000 years after his life on earth, as the best example of caring the world has ever seen.

"Both the natural world and the Bible clearly reveal a conflict between good and evil. The Bible, however, takes us behind the scenes and exposes the cause and provides a magnificent and almost unbelievable solution. Here, truth is truly stranger than fiction. The Bible is not as hard to understand as many suppose. Simply get a contemporary version and read it with an open mind, asking God to reveal Himself to you. The one prerequisite is to want to discover the basic truths of where we come from and where we're headed. If you're interested in more information from the Christian perspective, contact a Christian minister, join a small Bible study group, or just read the

Bible carefully for yourself. Most beginners find reading the stories of Jesus in the New Testament the best place to start.

"For now, let me share with you a couple of Biblical promises that are major stress buffers for me." These passages appeared on the screen:

> I already know the plans I have for you. I will help you, not hurt you. I will give you a future and a hope. You will call on me and I will answer. You will talk to me and I will listen.
>
> — Jeremiah 29:11-12

> Let not your heart be troubled. You believe in God, so trust me...I want you to have the same inner peace that I have—not the kind of peace that the world gives, but that abiding peace with the Father that only I can give. Don't be afraid of Him, because He loves you.
>
> — Jesus in John 14: 1, 27

> You will keep him in perfect peace whose mind is centred on you and who puts his trust in you.
>
> — Isaiah 26:3
>
> (all excerpts from The Clear Word)

As Cindy read the Bible passages, Sue thought, *Those are really encouraging and positive thoughts. I need to get a Bible and explore this whole area of life. I wonder how Bob is relating to this? He has never been one to take religion very seriously. It would be nice to explore this together.*

"Well, it's time for a break," Cindy announced. "Take twenty minutes, get some fresh air, and enjoy the refreshments."

Pam made her way over to Cindy with a number of questions. As Bob and Sue moved toward the refreshment table, Dale joined them and said, "Sue, thanks so much for your visit with Pam. She really appreciated it and it has definitely helped her begin the process of getting some control back into her life. I've been very concerned for some time now. She's been overcommitted for a long time but she hasn't been able to see it. Somehow, something you said got through, and she is beginning to address the problem."

"Glad to hear that," Sue replied. "I knew she was serious when she indicated she was going to make some changes. You and I can both be supportive as she makes the needed adjustments, but she has to make the decisions. She's on the edge of burnout." Just then, a friend from years back saw Sue and came over. Sue excused herself to visit. Bob and Dale, orange juice in hand, went outside for some fresh air.

"Bob," asked Dale, "do you play golf?"

"A little," Bob admitted. "But it's been years. I've been so obsessed with work that I haven't taken time for leisure and hobbies. This I need to change."

"Good. Let's get together sometime soon and have a game."

"That's a great idea," Bob agreed. "But remember, I'm very rusty and may even need some coaching."

"That's OK. I'm just learning myself. Most of the guys where I play are so much better, I feel very uncomfortable playing with them. I need someone who plays more at my level."

Bob and Dale had a great time visiting, and eventually set a date for a game of golf one night after work. As they walked back into the room, Bob thought to himself, *This seminar is about more than stress management. It actually involves a total lifestyle plan. This includes making friends and strengthening our personal support systems. Sue has already made a number of new friends that are becoming a significant part of her support system. I'll do the same, and Dale will be one of the first. This seminar has definitely been worth the price both in money and time!*

PRACTICAL TIPS for Giving Thanks for the Soup

- developing an attitude of gratitude
- exploring your spirituality
- counting your blessings
- being positive and optimistic
- offering thanks
- visualizing positive outcomes
- praying
- letting go and letting God
- not judging, but blessing
- nurturing yourself and others
- meditating
- being available
- granting grace
- giving the benefit of the doubt
- trusting—yourself, others, God
- loving unconditionally
- accepting unconditionally
- being content
- reading a spiritual book

Stress Management Principles

- Pinpoint and recognize the main stress producers in your life and take appropriate action—now!

- Develop an awareness of how stress is affecting you and listen to your body's stress-warning signals.

- Learn to control the stress response by calling a time out, breathing deeply, analyzing the situation, looking for humour and cutting yourself some slack.

- Learn the relaxation response and activate it often.

- Get regular daily physical activity.

- Humour is a wonderful stress buffer. Begin immediately to create a humour survival kit and use it regularly.

- Eat a wide variety of natural, plant-based foods (including some raw) for maximum energy and endurance.

- Avoid addictive drugs and resolve deep-seated stressors, such as low self-worth, grief, guilt, negative emotions, negative attitudes, unnatural anxiety and hopelessness.

- Develop an attitude of gratitude. Be thankful. Cultivate and enjoy your spirituality. Trust and nurture a personal relationship with God.

Eat The Soup Slowly And Enjoy It!

Controlling the pace

WHEN Cindy called the group back together she set the mood with a few lines of humour:

- There will be no crisis next week. My schedule is already full.

- Please be patient with me: I only work here because I am too old for a paper route, too young for a pension, and too tired to have an affair!

- Did you know that...

  ...it is illegal to set a trap for a mouse in California without a hunting license.

  ...a Belvedere, California, ordinance was written this way: "No dog shall be in public without its master on a leash."

...in the Pine Island District of Minnesota, a man must tip his hat when passing a cow.

...in Colorado Springs, Colorado, the law upholds a dog's right to one bite.

...singing out of tune in North Carolina is against the law.

Bob and Sue took their seats as the group was enjoying a good laugh. As they settled down, Cindy was saying, "Let's review. We have now cooled off the soup by learning to:

1. Let the soup sit, by controlling the stress response.
2. Thin the soup, by mastering relaxation.
3. Stir the soup, by exercising regularly.
4. Play with the soup, using humour.
5. Make sure the soup is nutritious, by eating wisely for strength, energy, and endurance.
6. Beware of poison in the soup, by avoiding dangerous drugs and resolving deep-seated stress.
7. Give thanks for the soup, by developing the "attitude of gratitude."

Now we are ready to:

8. Eat the soup slowly and enjoy it! by controlling the pace.

"Have you noticed how some people eat their soup too fast? Have you ever done that? I've been guilty of eating too fast and not savouring the moment. Recently, while visiting my mom, I was hungry and in a hurry, with a number of things on my mind. Mom had just made some delicious new muffins. She was anxious that I sample one and give an opinion. Because I was hungry and mentally preoccupied, I ate it in such a rush that when mom asked me how it was, I couldn't answer. My mind was somewhere else and I ate that muffin without actually tasting it! Unfortunately, many people live life like this—without taking the time to enjoy it.

"Our final stress management principle is to allow yourself time to eat the soup slowly. Take time to enjoy life. Smell a few roses. Play with some puppies. Enjoy the kids. Concentrate on making a life, not a living. Learn to enjoy the moment. As someone said, *Today is a gift; that is why it is called the present!*

"This leads us naturally into the area of getting adequate rest. Proper rest is an essential stress buffer and healer. An ancient philosopher put it this way: *Take rest; a field that has rested gives a bountiful crop.* It is so true. We need regular times for rest if we are going to operate at optimum. We need regular:

- **Daily Rest:** 7 to 10 hours of sleep (naps as needed)

- **Weekly Rest:** One full day off (sometimes two is better)

- **Yearly Rest:** A major restful, restorative vacation and/or a number of mini-vacations

"When I shared this with a class recently," continued Cindy, "a lady spoke up and said, 'What planet are you from?' She obviously couldn't conceive of this being practical on planet earth.

"However, who decides whether you get enough sleep at night? Unless you have a newborn baby at home, or live in a very noisy part of town, who decides? Who decides if you take one full day a week off for rest? Who decides if your vacation is restful and restorative? In most of the cases, you do! Of course!"

Bob's mind was racing as usual but this point had really made an impact. He thought, *This is so simple, yet for years I've neglected it. I've been working too many hours during the day, and then late into the night. Recently, it's been seven days a week, putting in seventy or eighty hours. No wonder I'm exhausted!*

As Bob mused, he could remember going on a month-long vacation and sleeping most of it because he was so exhausted. *I was ready for a holiday by the time the vacation was over*, he thought. *This must change.*

On the spot, Bob decided that only in extreme emergencies would he get caught in this trap again and even then he would explore other possibilities first.

Cindy had taken a number of questions by the time Bob refocused. Someone was saying, "I'm too anxious to sleep. My mind seems to pick up speed when I begin to relax. What can I do?"

As Cindy was about to give a response, another participant spoke up and said, "Cindy, can I share my experience with that problem?"

"Sure, go ahead," she said.

"I primarily came to this class hoping to get some help with my sleeping. I hadn't slept a full night in months and it was becoming a major problem. Anxiety had never been a serious problem for me until a few months ago. I became anxious and got more anxious, with chronic fatigue aggravating the situation. It was a vicious cycle and I knew that my lack of stress-coping skills was a major part of the problem. I must admit that I was not impressed with the first two sessions of this seminar. It all seemed too simplistic, especially the exercise and humour part. I had tried relaxation and a number of mind-over-body techniques but nothing seemed to work. To make a long story short, I decided to try the principles you were sharing. After all, what did I have to lose and I had already paid the fee.

"Some of the principles you've taught us, like paying attention to nutrition, I've been doing for years. However, physical exercise has been a weak link as I don't enjoy any kind of exercise. The evidence on the benefits of exercise made me face the reality that I should at least start walking. I had the option of walking outside in the fresh air and I began doing this on a daily basis. I also started looking for some good humour. I had heard of humour therapy but had never taken it very seriously.

"Of all the things that I've done, including taking a variety of powerful drugs, physical exercise has been the best anxiety tonic for me. At first, it seemed I didn't have the physical energy to walk for twenty minutes but I just made myself do it. It was like taking nasty-tasting medicine. The first week was extremely hard, and I am sure I walked less than half a mile each day. I almost quit a number of times. The only thing that kept me going was the fact that I did feel better after the walk than before. Just getting out and starting was the difficult part.

"Well, it's been just over two weeks and I can hardly believe the benefits. I'm now walking up to an hour a day and looking forward to it. I'm already sleeping much better. Exercise seems to dissolve my anxiety and depression. It seems that exercise, combined with relaxation, works really well for me. I'm now better able to recognize and deal with some deep-seated stressors that are the root of my anxiety problems. This seminar has been great for me and may even have saved my life because depression was leading me to despair. The principles you are sharing are so simple that we are in danger of overlooking their power."

"Thanks for that endorsement," Cindy said. "Does that help in answering your question?"

"Yes," the questioner replied. "I've been avoiding exercise. It seems that after a day at the office, I don't have the energy to go exercising, even walking. But I guess I need to start."

"For anxiety and depression, exercise is definitely one of the best tonics," continued Cindy. "Efforts put into physical exercise are always rewarded with increased energy levels. This is because it increases blood circulation, which in turn supplies the cells with more oxygen and nutrients to create more energy. This is a very typical exercise story; I hear similar ones often. Combine physical exercise with the other principles we have shared and you'll be a winner in the stress and anxiety battle.

"This story also illustrates that we must decide and take action if we are to change lifestyle habits. We must also recognize that there are no shortcuts to optimum health and well-being. It will take a bit of effort but the results are well worth it. It's amazing how a little extra time taking care of our bodies can save us so much in the long run.

"Recently, I visited with a friend who runs a three-week, live-in, lifestyle-conditioning centre. He sees remarkable progress and recovery from major lifestyle illness, primarily with exercise and nutritional changes. I asked him if it is possible to develop healthful, fast-food recipes. His reaction was quick and disturbing. This is what he told me.

"'We can do that only to a point. Then we either take the time to prepare healthy meals or we take the time later to have a stroke or heart attack or to die prematurely. People often tell me that they do not have the time to exercise or to cook properly. I simply say, then plan time to be sick, because it will happen prematurely and you will have no choice in the matter. It is your decision. Either take the time to cook and eat properly, and get adequate exercise, or spend months or years in a wheel chair. The choice, in most cases, is yours.' His answer was shocking and blunt, but very true. The principles we're sharing do take some time and effort, but they're time-tested and true, and very inexpensive."

Cindy took a number of other questions and then said, "Finally, let's talk about enjoying life. Joy is a choice. Yes, joy is a choice," she repeated. "Joy is a choice that always comes easier when you are rested. There may be some here who, because of their life experience, may question the fact that joy is a choice. Let me illustrate with a story.

"I have a friend who is now married and in his late thirties. We first met when he was in his early twenties and was single and carefree. He is one of these high-energy, outgoing, fun-loving characters for whom life always seems to be a party. In fact, if you're having a bad day or are depressed, he's the kind of person whose joy and exuberance for life can upset you.

"I'll call him Max. Max would often drop by our house, usually unannounced, and tell us all the exciting things happening at that moment in his life. There was always something interesting happening to him. We didn't mind his dropping in, as he had become part of the family and he was such a joy to have around.

"Well, this particular morning, at about 9 a.m., Max came in all excited about something. It just happened that a mutual friend of ours was visiting at the time. Now this friend was just the opposite of Max. Her life was a complex mix of problems, and nearly every day for her was a bad day. Her greatest delight in life seemed to be to destroy your day with all her troubles and depression. Well, right in the middle of one of her doom and gloom stories, in comes Max, full of joy, energy and excitement. Ignoring the seriousness of the moment, most likely because he knew the situation needed some lightening up, he told us all about the great thing that had just happened to him.

"The lady visiting with us took all this joy and excitement for about as long as she could. Then, looking directly at Max, said in a sarcastic tone, 'Every day is great for you, isn't it?' Max reacted almost immediately. Looking her straight in the eye, he said, 'Yes, every day is a great day for me *because three years ago I decided that every day was going to be a great day!*'

"You have to know some of his history to fully appreciate this response. At about age six, his parents separated and, over the next ten years, Max and his older brother moved from one foster home to another. They experienced a variety of abusive situations. Yet, at some point during his teen years, Max resolved the abuse issues and decided that every day was going to be a good day. Even with all the ups and downs of life, including raising a young family, for Max, every day is still a great day. In fact, I've kept in touch with Max over the years, and I recall only a couple of times when he was really feeling down, and then only because he was exhausted. I've said to him at these times, 'Max, you must slow down and review your priorities.'

"Joy *is* a choice," Cindy repeated. "Joy is a choice that comes easier when you are rested.

"We could talk about this for quite some time, but I think you get the point. It's time now for your group discussion. First, we want to give you an opportunity to act on the information you have learned tonight and then share for a few minutes with those in your group. Turn to this page in your workbook." She flashed this now-familiar page on the screen:

Improving The Recipe For A Better Soup

My Action Plan For This Week

- Start: _____

- Stop: _____

- Keep: _____

"Tonight, we've discussed giving thanks for the soup and getting adequate rest. Again, it's decision time! Many of you are making great progress. Just like last week, in the blank beside *Start*, write one thing that you are going to start doing immediately to manage your stress better. Then, beside *Stop*, write one thing you are going to immediately stop doing because it is not helping you manage your stress. Finally, because we have all survived, and are doing some things right, write beside *Keep*, something you are going to keep on doing because it has been helping you manage your stress effectively. You have a few minutes to do this exercise."

The room went quiet as the group, now familiar with the exercise, individually considered their options and made life-changing decisions. After about five minutes, Cindy said, "Let's divide into our groups again. Please stay with the same group. You're getting to know each other better and, I hope, are developing a mutual support system. Once again, when you're together, share a joke or two and then discuss what you wrote in the decision exercise. We have a little extra time tonight so don't rush."

Both couples, Bob and Sue, and Dale and Pam, were developing a mutual support system, and all four looked forward to this part of the evening. Pam led off with a joke. She was an outgoing character and because she had been relaxing the last few days, had found a good joke book and had brought a couple of her favourites. They all had a good laugh, with Bob adding a few jokes of his own.

When they discussed their decisions, spiritual concerns seemed to dominate. Bob actually raised the issue. He had been surprised with the strong emphasis on spirituality in tonight's session. "It's an area I don't understand," he said. "My only positive experience with religion is a business associate who is so honest, positive, and helpful that I'd trust him with my life. He always returns thanks for his food, even in a restaurant, and he has the best business sense I've seen. I think he's a Christian of some kind. But I have never really explored that area much. Have any of you?"

Dale relayed his experience. "I grew up in a Christian home and at one time was very close to God. However, I haven't thought much about it recently. I was also surprised at the emphasis tonight—

pleasantly surprised, I might add. I can see that with the deep-seated areas of stress, like guilt and grief, it would be very helpful." He looked at Pam. "Maybe we need to return to this area of our life and access the strength there."

Pam responded positively, and the discussion revolved around how to find the truth in all the confusion. Sue surprised herself when she expressed her decision to find a Bible and read it for herself, as Cindy suggested. Dale recommended a version that he had found particularly helpful. Both Dale and Pam had at least a working knowledge of spiritual things, whereas for Bob and Sue, it was a new area to explore.

Then Pam gave a report on her progress. She was excited about her two weeks off work. Sue offered her teenage girls as possible baby sitters for Dale and Pam, if they needed a break. Just as their time ran out, Sue mentioned her bike rides with Cindy.

Pam said, "I haven't biked in years."

"Would you like to join us tomorrow? Sue asked. "If you don't have a bike, you can use mine and I'll use Bob's."

Pam accepted the offer just as Cindy announced that group time was up.

"Next week is our last session," Cindy reminded everyone. "You will not want to miss it. Dr. Morgan will be back with us to discuss how to avoid and how to recover from burnout. His personal experience with burnout gives him a helpful understanding of the issue. Of course, we will have graduation as well, so make sure you are here. Good night, and have a great week."

PRACTICAL TIPS for Eating the Soup Slowly and Enjoying It

- getting enough rest
- choosing joy
- being still and resting
- scheduling play time
- taking a nap
- changing your environment
- taking mini-vacations
- doing your best and then stopping
- tackling one thing at a time
- giving in occasionally
- talking to a friend
- not overworking
- making a "done" list
- just saying NO!
- being available
- not oversleeping
- turning off the beeper
- turning off the TV
- relishing good memories
- enjoying anticipation
- simplifying holidays (e.g., Christmas)
- car pooling and enjoying the ride
- choosing joyful living
- choosing not to answer the phone

The applause made it clear that the group was enjoying and benefiting from the seminar. Bob and Sue were in no rush to leave, and visited with a number of people. Bob had some questions for Cindy and then invited her to join them on Sunday, when Caroline was going to spend the day with them. He explained later, to Sue, that having someone like Cindy with them might be helpful in dealing with the grief issue.

As they drove home, Bob said, "It's been another good evening. I'm especially interested in next week's session on burnout. I know that I was getting close. By the way, I like your idea of getting a Bible. I'd like to take a look at it."

Sue nodded. She was feeling especially thankful. Life for the Picco family was beginning to take on a more natural flow. Things hadn't slowed down, but life seemed to be more manageable, and she was beginning to discover where she might find the answers to some of her deeper questions.

Stress Management Principles

- Pinpoint and recognize the main stress producers in your life and take appropriate action—now!

- Develop an awareness of how stress is affecting you and listen to your body's stress-warning signals.

- Learn to control the stress response by calling a time out, breathing deeply, analyzing the situation, looking for humour and cutting yourself some slack.

- Learn the relaxation response and activate it often.

- Get regular daily physical activity.

- Humour is a wonderful stress buffer. Begin immediately to create a humour survival kit and use it regularly.

- Eat a wide variety of natural, plant-based foods (including some raw) for maximum energy and endurance.

- Avoid addictive drugs and resolve deep-seated stressors, such as low self-worth, grief, guilt, negative emotions, negative attitudes, unnatural anxiety and hopelessness.

- Develop an attitude of gratitude. Be thankful. Cultivate and enjoy your spirituality. Trust and nurture a personal relationship with God.

- Live life at a leisurely pace and get adequate rest. Consciously and deliberately choose joy.

What If...You Already Ate The Soup Too Hot?

Avoiding or recovering from burnout

OVER the past few weeks, breakfast time had become a more relaxed and enjoyable family time in the Picco home. Bob and Sue were both deliberately getting up a bit earlier and allowing time for a more leisurely meal. The children were still wandering into the kitchen at different times and were pleasantly surprised to find dad and mom eating together. The food that Sue was taking extra time to prepare was smelling more tempting at that early hour of the day, even for finicky teenage palates. Bob was obviously more relaxed in the morning and didn't rush off to work as early. In fact, he'd begun driving the kids to school and was enjoying it.

The morning after the seminar, Sue got so relaxed doing some reading that she forgot all about her biking appointment with Pam and Cindy. "I can't believe this," she said to herself, as she looked out the window and saw Pam parking her car. "I'm getting too relaxed. I must find my to-do list and start using it again."

Sue met Pam at the door. "Come in. I got so involved in reading this book on cooking natural foods that I forgot all about the time. I need a few minutes to get ready."

"That's okay," said Pam. "I'm a few minutes early. I have all my housework done. It actually feels good to be caught up, although I'm constantly thinking that I should be doing something. My mom is visiting for a few days and she's taking care of the children for the morning. I'm in no rush."

Sue mused, *If only I had half her energy—even when she's tired!*

Cindy was waiting for them as they rode up about ten minutes late. "Did you ladies sleep in with all this extra relaxation?" she asked jokingly.

"No." Sue apologized. "I got so involved with that natural-foods book you loaned me that I forgot all about the time. If Pam hadn't come along, I may have missed our ride."

They had a great ride in the park. The weather was sunny and warm. It was obvious to Sue that Pam and Cindy had been friends for some time. The morning flew by and because none of them had pressing commitments, they decided to have lunch together at a little vegetarian restaurant near the park. Cindy, a long time vegetarian, had discovered it while out biking alone.

"I'm becoming a bit of a vegetarian myself," Sue said. "This book I'm reading gives some good reasons why meat is not the best food."

"They have an excellent meatless burger at this little restaurant," said Cindy. "If you try it, I think you'll be pleasantly surprised at how good it is on their multi-grain bun."

It didn't take much convincing for both Sue and Pam to try the meatless burger, and both were surprised at how good it tasted. Pam said, "This is excellent. I've had some meatless burgers before, but this is exceptional. Dale and the kids wouldn't even know this wasn't meat."

"In our upcoming nutrition class, we'll be teaching how to make meatless burgers plus a number of other low-fat, plant-based foods that are a great meat replacement. Have either of you thought about taking our nutrition class?" Cindy asked.

"Bob and I are already signed up." Sue was enthusiastic. "I was pleasantly surprised when Bob volunteered to come along. He's taking this health thing seriously."

"I'm glad to hear it," said Cindy. "He's looking better every week. When he started the stress seminar he was on the verge of burnout. It'll take months for him to fully recover."

Pam asked, "Do you teach the cooking class at any other times? I've thought about attending, but evenings are not good for me."

"Oh, yes," Cindy replied. "Just give me a call. I don't teach that class, but the people who do, have a variety of times. By the way, get Dale to come with you. Men tend to think they don't need this material but they do. It will make changes in your family's diet much easier if dad is on board from the start."

A few minutes later, Pam had to excuse herself and go home. Sue was about to leave when Cindy asked, "Could you fill me in a bit about Sunday? Bob invited me to come over for the day. He said you've invited a young lady who lost her husband recently and may need some help with grief."

"I think *our* family might also need help with the grief," Sue commented. "Caroline seems to be doing fine, considering her situation. We invited her over because her husband worked for us before he died suddenly of a heart attack." Sue told Cindy the whole story and said, "I think Bob invited you over thinking that if any difficult questions about death and grief arise, your presence would be very helpful."

"Thanks for the details," said Cindy. "I'm glad to be of any help. Can I bring something?"

"How about a few of those veggie burgers. We just won't tell anyone they're vegetarian and see what the reaction is," Sue said as she got up to leave.

"Glad to. I'll also bring buns and relish. See you then."

On Saturday afternoon, the entire family was involved with getting ready for Caroline and her family. It had been a long time since Sue had seen such a united family activity. The children were excited about taking care of Caroline's children and had several games planned. Bob was a bit anxious because this was a major reminder of Gary's loss—both to him personally and to the business. Cindy's offer to bring food helped Sue tremendously and allowed her to relax. She was really looking forward to the vegetarian experiment.

About eleven o'clock Sunday morning, Caroline and her children arrived. Her son, Robin, was seven and in grade one; Crystal was five and would begin school in the fall. Sue's heart felt deep pain for Caroline as a single parent with the responsibility of raising two children alone. Caroline, however, seemed up to the challenge and it was obvious that she had accepted the fact of the loss and was beginning to move on.

Cindy arrived around noon with her food. By one o'clock, everything was ready and everyone was enjoying a great meal in the backyard. The weather was super. The Picco teenagers were doing a great job entertaining the younger children. Suddenly, Sue's oldest daughter, Karen, said, "Mom, these aren't meat burgers. They're just like the ones they have at that vegetarian restaurant just outside the park."

"And how would you know about that restaurant?" asked a surprised Sue.

"Because my friends and I go there all the time. We prefer eating the non-meat burgers. In fact, I think I'm going to be a vegetarian like many of my friends."

"Are many of your friends vegetarian?" asked Cindy.

"Quite a few," answered Karen. "It's quite popular in our school. Meat is getting less safe to eat with all the diseases, like mad cow, and do you know that it takes 16 pounds of grain and soybeans to produce only one pound of meat? Lots of kids are cutting back on meat or avoiding it altogether."

Everyone was impressed with Karen's knowledge of the issue and how far she'd progressed in changing her diet. Sue could recognize a partner for change when she saw one, and here was one right at home—her own daughter!

Bob spoke up. "Are you sure this isn't meat? It sure tastes like it to me."

Sue was delighted. Bob actually liked the meatless burgers and no one missed the meat or complained. *That's progressive change!* she thought.

The afternoon was fun for everyone, with games and a variety of activities. Bob and Cindy had a long visit with Caroline. Cindy was quite impressed at how well she was doing in handling both the grief and the kids all by herself.

"She has a strong family support system, a positive attitude, some good stress-coping skills, and a deep personal faith relationship with God." As Cindy was leaving, she continued, "The loss of a spouse is the single greatest stressor but she's handling it very well. Continue to keep in touch with her and be there when she has a special need, and give her your support."

Encouraged by Cindy's comments, Bob later mentioned to Caroline how they all missed Gary at work and how he'd been such a valuable employee.

"Gary really enjoyed the time he worked with you," Caroline said quietly. "He especially appreciated the confidence you placed in him even though he was so young. By the way, do you have any openings at work? With Crystal going to school I've been thinking of going back to work myself. After all, someone has to be the breadwinner."

"That could be a real possibility," said Bob. "Come by sometime and let's have a talk. Bring your resume. We're always needing good people and, if at all possible, we'll find you a place, either part-time or full-time."

"I'll do that soon. You've both been so kind and helpful," said Caroline. "The kids have had a great time here today. They miss Gary so much. He always took time to play with them every night, even when he was very tired. They were his pride and joy."

"If you ever need a baby sitter," offered Sue, "I or one of the kids would gladly come and help at no cost."

"Thanks for the offer," answered Caroline, recognizing that they only wanted to be helpful. "But with so many of our family in town that's seldom a problem. Just keep us in your prayers as we go through this time of adjustment."

There it is again, Bob thought. *Keep us in your prayers. What does she mean? I've got to figure out this spiritual stuff.*

After Caroline and the children had gone, the Piccos held a family council. Everyone was very excited and quite proud of themselves, and rightly so. They all felt positive about supporting a family in crisis and helping them deal with such a terrible loss.

"Mom," said Karen, "I think they're all doing quite well, considering. I'm not so sure I would be doing so well if that had happened in our family."

"Well, it's surprising the inner strength we have when we need it," Sue replied.

Tuesday night came quickly. It was the last session of the stress seminar and, in preparation, Bob and Sue had their regular bike ride together. They were now doing about twelve miles and both felt they could go on cycling all evening.

"We should plan a longer bike ride some Sunday," Bob suggested, as they headed for the shower. "I think we can handle some extra exercise on the weekends. What do you say?"

"Sure, and bring the children?"

"OK. Let's plan it," Bob agreed.

As they were going out the driveway, Bob suggested they try out the vegetarian restaurant. "Maybe we can try a new dish of some kind."

"You sound courageous tonight," Sue said as they drove away, "for someone who doesn't like to try new foods."

"Well," Bob said, "I feel like exploring some of these food changes. It may not be as hard as we think."

Sue could hardly believe her ears. Something good was happening to Bob and she just had to help keep it alive. They enjoyed a delicious vegetarian noodle dish that was heavier than they'd planned. Nevertheless, they decided they'd return to this restaurant again soon, and experiment some more.

There was an almost festive mood in the air as the group gathered for the last session. It was obvious that most participants had made considerable progress in handling their stress over the last month. While attendance was down a bit, compared with the first couple of sessions—a few people had dropped out—the majority had stayed and now, of course, would graduate.

Cindy called the class to order right on time. She took a few questions and then introduced Dr. Morgan, who moved right into the topic for the evening.

"Tonight," he began, "we are going to discuss the seven stages of burnout, how to avoid it, and how to recover. First of all, what is burnout? There are numerous definitions. Here are three that I hope will give us a better understanding.

A debilitating psychological condition brought about by unrelieved work stress, which results in depleted energy reserves, lowered resistance to illness, increased dissatisfaction and pessimism and increased absenteeism and inefficiency at work.

— Veninga & Spradley, **The Work Stress Connection**

A state of fatigue or frustration brought about by devotion to a cause, way of life, or relationship that failed to produce the expected reward.

— H. Freudenberger, **The High Cost of High Achievement**

A progressive loss of idealism, energy, and purpose experienced by people in the helping professions.

— J. Edelwich and A. Brodsky, **Burnout**

"At highest risk of burnout are the following:

- Idealists, who approach their work with unrealistically high expectations.
- Perfectionists, with unrealistic expectations of themselves and others.
- The helping professionals (teachers, pastors, nurses, social workers), who face high demands on their emotional energy but have limited control of the situation.

"One of the first concepts that we need to understand is the difference between excessive stress and burnout," continued Dr. Morgan. "Excessive stress is the overuse of our coping capacities caused by too much activity and change. Many come to this seminar experiencing excessive stress and think it is burnout. Others come experiencing actual burnout or the nearly complete depletion of their coping reserves. Excessive stress results in fatigue, mild depression, physical illness, reduced mental alertness, and a number of the stress-warning signals that Cindy discussed at the beginning of this seminar. Burnout, on the other hand, results in complete physical and mental exhaustion that leads to disillusionment, cynicism and self-depreciation. The individual is simply overwhelmed by life and cannot function normally.

"Yes, even the wise can burn out. The wisest king of ancient times experienced burnout. His comments reflect fully the feelings and sentiments of those in advanced burnout. King Solomon wrote, "Meaningless! Meaningless!" says the teacher. "Utterly meaningless! Everything is meaningless." I can relate to those words. When I was in the midst of burnout a few years ago, they were some of my favourite lines because they expressed exactly the way I felt at the time. Life for me seemed hopeless and meaningless at best.

"There is much confusion between excessive stress and burnout. I see it all the time in my work with people who deal with stress. Here is a story that illustrates the difference and shows how many people confuse the two. As I was recovering from burnout, a friend who knew of my illness called me one day and said, 'I am burned out. I have a friend in Florida so I am going there for a week to recover. I have talked to my boss and made arrangements but I need to talk to someone who understands. Could you meet me at the airport and have a talk?'

"We met at the airport and after about five minutes I could tell that he was not in burnout. He was what I call *browned down*. He was tired and exhausted. He was feeling the negative results of excessive stress but he was not even close to burnout. He had been dealing with some very difficult work situations and needed to get away and get some rest. Because I knew both him and his work well, I encouraged him to take the vacation and get some rest. Then I suggested that when he returned home, that he slow down and concentrate on the work that he does best and enjoys the most, while letting some of the major problems he was dealing with sit for a while. He took my advice, and to my knowledge has never experienced burnout.

"Recently, I read of a man describing his burnout experience while in a helping profession and he said that, while recovering, he went back to school and finished a doctorate degree. My immediate reaction was, 'This man was not in burnout but had browned down.' He may have been at about stage four or five of burnout when he decided on a change, but had gotten some rest and recovered significantly before entering the program. You cannot function adequately enough, while in burnout, to undertake doctoral-level classes and research. In burnout, your concentration levels are extremely limited at best."

Dr. Morgan's remarks clarified for Sue where *she* had been. She realized that she had recently been experiencing some negative results of excessive stress but that she was not near burnout. Both Bob and Pam were definitely experiencing more than excessive stress and may have been very close to burnout. However, Sue had caught herself in time and had quit full-time work.

Then Sue heard Dr. Morgan say, "Before moving on to the actual stages of burnout, I would like to tell you briefly about my experience. Burnout can be caused by a number of things: overwork, mismatch for a job or relationship, excessive internal or external pressures, et cetera. For me it was simply overwork. I had worked too many seventy-hour and eighty-hour weeks during the nearly fifteen years in a helping profession and my body simply couldn't take it any longer. What put me over the edge was a particularly busy summer, and I went into exhaustion.

"I had been having a number of serious stress signals for years but had not recognized them. Many people make this same mistake. One night, I woke up and was certain there were fleas in the bed because I was itchy all over. There were no fleas, and the itch lasted for about an hour. A few months later, I got the shingles, a disease related to stress. Yet I did not feel stressed or overworked.

"It was July 1st, the beginning of that extremely busy summer. A vacation would not come until the middle of September. I was in a store when my entire body began to shake. By the time I got home, I was shaking uncontrollably. Reluctant to go to the hospital, I just lay down on the bed, and the whole bed shook. This lasted for about six hours and quit just as abruptly as it had begun. Had I known then what I know now, I would have taken major stress leave immediately. Instead, I moved on into that summer with eighty to ninety hours of work per week.

"By September, I was beyond exhaustion and well into burnout but still did not realize it. Mid month, we left on a two-month camping holiday. Our children were both preschoolers at the time. Now you must recognize that stress can do some strange things. You can manage it quite well until you begin to relax and then it hits you, and it hits hard. We were not three hours out of town when a depression settled down over me that I would not wish on my worst enemy. I did not have a positive thought for at least three weeks. I could not concentrate or read. I came as close to a complete *hitting-of-the-wall* burnout as you can, without doing it. Except for the grace of God, I would have. I should have been under some kind of professional care but did not realize the seriousness of the situation.

"After being away for two months, I thought I was ready to go back to work. But, after a week on the job, I realized I could not function. I finally went to see a physician and learned I was still experiencing serious depression. I slowed down, and practiced the principles that Cindy has been sharing with you. I was fortunate and was able to recover without having to take medication. The complete process, however, took about three years. It took me fifteen years to get to that burned-out state, and there is no quick recovery. I share this with you simply to show that recovery is possible, and you need simply to make the needed lifestyle changes. A major benefit of the burnout experience is that now I know exactly when I am getting overextended and can take the appropriate action quickly.

"Well, enough of my story. Let us get into the seven stages of burnout," continued Morgan.

"First, let's take a couple of questions," Cindy interjected. "At this point, some people have some concerns."

As Dr. Morgan answered questions, Bob was thinking about his situation. He realized that if he stayed on the road he was travelling he would have a similar experience. *As it is, I must be in the advanced stages of burnout*, he thought. *I still have several serious stress signals daily, like headaches and inability to concentrate.*

"Okay," said Dr. Morgan, "those are good questions. You have a sharp class here, Cindy, but we must move on.

"We are always in one of the seven stages that we will now discuss. The first stage is where we want to be most of the time. It is where we enjoy positive stress. It's the **honeymoon** stage. This is a period of high energy and satisfaction. You are full of enthusiasm and excitement. You can work hard and long and use up a great amount of energy, but you never feel exhausted, just exhilarated! Any stress you feel is the type of stress that keeps you sharp and does not wear you down.

"An example of the honeymoon stage would be a new graduate ready to take on the new job that he or she has been preparing for. It's like owning a new car. The honeymoon is the stage where the car is new and fresh off the car lot. The plastic is still on the seats, with that fresh, new smell permeating the entire car. At this stage, most of the stress in your life is positive stress and you begin to develop the coping skills needed for the particular stresses of your life. For example, if you are successful at work and your abilities are matched to the demands of your job, you can stay in the honeymoon for as long as you work. In relationships and marriage, if you develop caring and understanding interpersonal skills, the honeymoon can last for a lifetime. Yes, you can stay in the honeymoon stage indefinitely! Here is some especially good news for some of you. It is also possible to be in serious burnout and yet return to and stay in the honeymoon stage!"

Bob didn't miss that comment and he felt himself relax at the positive thought. *Who wouldn't love to be on a honeymoon?* he thought.

"The next two stages of burnout I call the warning stages. Stage two is the **tune-up** stage. This is where you have overdrawn on your energy supply. There is a vague feeling of loss, and some of the enthusiasm is gone. Challenge is beginning to be replaced by disillusionment. There isn't total dissatisfaction. The exhaustion and depression doesn't last long but neither does that creative burst of energy that once got you through the day. The result is inefficiency. You accomplish less with poorer quality. For example, the executive finds it increasingly difficult to make prompt decisions. Our car now needs a tune-up. You've had it for several months now, it's been driven several thousand miles and is beginning to use more fuel. It's less efficient and is not functioning as well as before. It simply needs a tune-up.

"Stage three is the **early warning** stage. For the car, this is where a few warning lights flash. Maybe it's the oil light or temperature light that flashes occasionally. They don't stay on but simply flash a warning. At this stage, its wise to check out the problem. It could save you many dollars later. At this stage of burnout, a number of stress-warning signals begin to appear. Now it's more than lack of enthusiasm. It's any number of physical symptoms, like headaches, indigestion or sleep difficulties. Emotional symptoms may or may not be recognizable at this stage—nervousness and anxiety for no good reason, boredom, edginess, et cetera. The body is saying *ouch!* It's beginning to react negatively to stress and to give a number of signals that help is needed. A good health check at this stage will prevent much grief later. You might feel a bit like the person who said, *I used up all my sick days so I'm calling in dead and I'd like three funeral days along with my weekend off!*

"Stage four, the **chronic symptom** stage, is the early stage or what I call first-degree burnout. In our car illustration, this is where the oil and temperature lights stay on! Wise motorists take the warnings seriously and immediately turn off the engine!

"You know you've reached stage-four of burnout when you are just as tired in the morning as you were the night before. Your tiredness has turned into chronic exhaustion. The physical symptoms become more pronounced. You become irritable. Your skin breaks out in hives or eczema. Dizzy spells, shortness of breath, pounding heart, changes in blood pressure may be common. Psychological symptoms also increase. You are emotionally exhausted and feel drained. You erupt in anger in situations that before would have caused only minor irritation. Depression rolls over you like a tidal wave and you can't escape. Get help immediately! You need a mechanic. You are in serious trouble and there are still three stages to go! Fortunate is the person who, at this stage, has a good friend who can tell him things he doesn't want to admit to himself. Most people at this stage can back out of the burnout spiral simply by making some lifestyle changes and practicing the eight ways to cool off the stress soup.

"Stage five is the **critical symptom** stage, or what I call second-degree burnout. In your car, this is a full dashboard alert! All the warning lights are on; it's similar to what happened on Apollo 13 when the Commander said, 'Houston, we have a problem.' At this stage you are in deep trouble and your symptoms have become critical. Chronic frustration and dissatisfaction are the rule of the day. Both physical and psychological symptoms intensify and/or increase in number. You may even visit with a doctor and have a number of tests, but physically, little is wrong. At this point, you become obsessed with your problems. Fear and depression are constant companions. Action is needed immediately, and professional help may be required to break the cycle. At this stage, a good counselor may be as helpful as a medical doctor.

"For myself," said Dr. Morgan, "I was somewhere between stages four and five for a number of years. The next stage, number six, is where I was when we left on the camping trip.

"Stages six and seven are the final stages and what I call third-degree burnout. Stage six is the **crisis** stage. This is where the engine begins to knock and rattle. Yes, some people will continue to drive their car when the engine is knocking and rattling. Likewise, people will continue to push themselves when they can hardly function. At this crisis stage, pessimism and cynicism develop, with a callous, insensitive disregard for people. Self-doubts and despair permeate your thinking. At this stage, you can be so negative and depressed that if someone comes on the television smiling and happy, you want to throw a rock at them. It is almost impossible to be positive at this stage. This is not a time to make major life-changing decisions like divorcing your spouse or quitting your job.

"At this stage, you feel like a trapped animal. An escape mentality develops: I've got to get out of this town, this job, this marriage; I've just got to get out of here. Getting help is critical because your physical and mental health are in serious jeopardy."

Bob looked at Sue and whispered, "I was at this stage a month ago and may still be. This is scary. What if this seminar hadn't come along? I shudder to think what might have happened!"

Sue acknowledged Bob's concerns and said, "We can be very thankful that you are on the road to understanding and recovery."

Dr. Morgan's next remark brought them back to the class. "If anyone here tonight is at this stage, you must take action now! You do not want to go on to stage seven. In fact, if you are at this stage and have access to some form of stress-leave at work, take advantage of it now! Don't talk to your boss first. Go and see your doctor first, put a recovery plan in place, then see your boss. I am very serious. At this stage, you are not much good at work anyway. You are probably more of a problem than you are a help. You will be of no help to yourself, your family or at work if you don't get help and get it quickly. Your long-term well-being is in serious jeopardy.

"Now, finally, comes stage seven, **hitting the wall**. This is when the engine blows! This is where you lose control of your life. You become completely dysfunctional and experience a total breakdown.

"*Hitting the wall* is a phrase that comes from the world of marathon running. It's the point where the runner experiences a devastating depletion of the muscle fuel known as glycogen. At this point, the body becomes dehydrated, the temperature rises to $44-45\,°C$ ($106-107\,°F$), and there is loss of blood volume. Muscle paralysis can occur, with dizziness, fainting and complete collapse, and it means having to drop out of the race. When people reach this stage of burnout, their adaptive energy is depleted just like the runner's glycogen. They lose control of their lives and, for some, it puts an end to their working careers forever. You meet some of these people on skid row, in prison or mental institutions. Others end their lives in suicide. Now you have a better understanding of why they're there. It is possible to hit the wall and recover but it is not probable. Any questions before we look at how we avoid or recover from burnout?"

While Dr. Morgan took questions, Pam leaned over to Sue and said, "I think I'm at stage five. A couple of months ago I'm sure I was at stage six. I fear what would have happened if I hadn't become reacquainted with Cindy and attended this class. I think I'm going to take a few more weeks off and maybe I'll quit politics for a few years."

"You're on the right track, Pam," Sue reassured. "Just keep evaluating your priorities and choosing the best and you'll eventually get back to the honeymoon stage!"

Then Bob spoke up and said to Dr. Morgan, "I'm glad I didn't know about these stages a month ago. At that time I was about to hit the wall and this news would have pushed me over. As it is, this information is scary and has added considerably to my frustration and despair. It's good now to see that I've recovered to stage six and can see a way to the light at the end of the tunnel."

"Some people," responded Morgan, "are like you, while others must have the hard facts before they actually see the seriousness of their situation. Remember to be patient in recovery. It took you a number of years to get to the crisis stage and it will take a minimum of a few months or a few years to achieve a complete recovery.

"Well, let's look at the process of how to recover. Actually, you have most of the basic tools already. The eight ways to cool off the stress soup are essential to both prevention as well as recovery from burnout. Here are a few additional hints.

"The operative words here are *take control*. Yes, for burnout, we can blame nobody but ourselves. Oh, I know we would like to blame someone or a number of individuals, but the buck stops with us. I can think of several individuals that I would like to blame but the hard truth is only *I* can take responsibility for my unbalanced lifestyle.

"It cannot be overemphasized that the primary secret in preventing, and, yes, also in recovering from, burnout is this: only *you* can take responsibility for your own life. Here is a list of six steps that will help you take control:

1. **Take control of your physical health** by giving your body a daily NEWSTART(© Weimar Institute) with:

   > Good Balanced Nutrition
   > Daily Physical Exercise
   > Plenty of Water (6 – 8 glasses a day)
   > Adequate Sunshine (20 minutes a day)
   > Practicing Temperance
   > A good supply of Fresh Air
   > Adequate Rest and Relaxation
   > Trust in God

2. **Take control of your thoughts and behaviours.** A number of studies have demonstrated how our thoughts affect our behaviours and vice versa. Focusing on positive, uplifting thoughts, will directly affect how we feel and act. Taking action, like physical exercise, will have a positive effect on our thoughts and dispel gloom and depression.

3. **Take control of your time, and plan each day**. Proper time management is a must. Simply allow yourself enough time for your priorities. For example, start each day slowly, positively, with a good breakfast, and with a good realistic and practical plan for the day. If you need additional help with time management, the best book I know on the subject is *First Things First* by Steven Covey.

4. **Take control of your work**. Change gears after work and cut back on excessive work hours. Studies clearly demonstrate that if you are working more than fifty-five hours per week, your efficiency drops drastically. Consistently working sixty to seventy hours a week is not wise because you are using up future energy and reducing your effectiveness. The practice of medical interns working superman hours just to survive medical school sets a poor example. Not only does this practice hurt the student's health, but sets a killing work pattern that, for many, lasts a lifetime.

5. **Take control of your relationships and develop an effective personal support system.** Learn how to deal with people, especially your family and fellow workers. Relationships do not happen automatically. Positive and meaningful relationships with your spouse, children or parents require significant time and effort. A personal support system means that you have three to five people that you can lean on when times get tough. If possible, some of these should be outside your immediate family and work group.

6. **Take control of your future**. Take an honest assessment of your goals and values, and develop a practical life plan. This will take some time but if you haven't done this, now is the time. Distorted values can cause much unnecessary stress. Gordon Dahl showed clearly why most people need to spend some time assessing their values. He said, 'Most middle-class North Americans tend to worship their work, work at their play and play at their worship. As a result, their meanings and values are distorted.' This is why some experience job burnout. You may have assessed your values

some time ago and need to do an update. If you need additional help with life planning, the best book I know is *The 7 Habits of Highly Effective People* by Steven Covey. You need to make sure that you are making a *life* and not just a *living*.

"We've covered a lot of material in the first half of this session and I know you need a break. First, one final thought on burnout. Earlier, I mentioned that even the wise can and do burn out, and we mentioned the ancient King Solomon. After recovering from burnout and regaining the honeymoon stage, he made the comment we have on the screen:"

So I decided there is nothing better than to enjoy food and drink and to find satisfaction in work. Then I realized that this pleasure is from the hand of God...So I commend the enjoyment of life.
— adapted from the words of King Solomon

After Dr. Morgan answered a few questions, Cindy came forward and said, "Let's thank Dr. Morgan for this excellent material." The audience broke out in appreciative applause that ended in a standing ovation.

As the clapping subsided, Cindy announced, "Enjoy the break and refreshments and we'll return for the final session in fifteen minutes."

Bob was feeling a bit overwhelmed as he headed towards the refreshment table. "You look like you just saw a ghost," Dale said as he approached Bob.

"Dale, I have just realized how close I came to hitting the wall and it's a very frightening experience," Bob said calmly. "I guess a miss is as good as a mile but I came just about as close as you can come to a complete burnout without having it! I hope our golf game is still on for tomorrow because I just decided that I'm taking the next month off and getting my life in order. This is priority number one!"

"You sound serious," Dale said. "Yes, our game is still on and if I can be your sounding board as you work through this, don't hesitate to ask."

"Thanks, Dale. You'll be hearing from me for sure," Bob replied. "I need all the friends I can find right now!"

Sue was amazed at the impact of this session on Bob. She knew they would be talking long into the night on this one.

Stress Management Principles

- Pinpoint and recognize the main stress producers in your life and take appropriate action—now!

- Develop an awareness of how stress is affecting you and listen to your body's stress-warning signals.

- Learn to control the stress response by calling a time out, breathing deeply, analyzing the situation, looking for humour and cutting yourself some slack.

- Learn the relaxation response and activate it often.

- Get regular daily physical activity.

- Humour is a wonderful stress buffer. Begin immediately to create a humour survival kit and use it regularly.

- Eat a wide variety of natural, plant-based foods (including some raw) for maximum energy and endurance.

- Avoid addictive drugs and resolve deep-seated stressors, such as low self-worth, grief, guilt, negative emotions, negative attitudes, unnatural anxiety and hopelessness.

- Develop an attitude of gratitude. Be thankful. Cultivate and enjoy your spirituality. Trust and nurture a personal relationship with God.

- Live life at a leisurely pace and get adequate rest. Consciously and deliberately choose joy.

- To avoid burnout, take control of your health, thoughts, behaviours, time, work, relationships, values and future, and consistently practice the 8 ways to cool off the stress soup!

SHAKE
SHAKE

ND 97

Chapter

12

Improving The Recipe For A Better Soup

Developing a personal action plan

THE break flew by too quickly for Bob. He needed a smoke but the lecture had so frightened him that he would not allow himself the luxury. He hadn't felt so confused and scared in a long, long time. When Cindy called the group back together, she saw a number of upset and agitated participants and was uncertain just how to proceed.

Finally, she spoke. "I noticed that for a number of you this last session was very upsetting and maybe even threatening. Don't be too hard on yourself. Simply realize that even if you have been or are in serious burnout, recognizing where you are puts you seventy-five percent down the road to recovery. In the early 1960s, President John F. Kennedy made a decision that, by the end of the decade, the USA would put a man on the moon and return him safely to earth. The technology to do that was not yet available, but America was seventy-five percent of the way to the moon simply by making that decision and the commitment that came with it. *Decision* and *commitment* will do the same for you!

"It's obvious that a number of you are struggling with the burnout material presented by Dr. Morgan. Let's take a few minutes, right now, and separate into our groups to discuss the material Dr. Morgan has shared."

The room suddenly became a beehive of activity as chairs were rearranged and animated discussions began. Cindy went around to each group and answered questions and gave counsel. By the time she got to Bob's group, everyone had shared their feelings about the session except Bob. He had been unusually quiet as Pam, Sue, and finally Dale shared their responses. For Dale and Sue, the session had been very enlightening, and any fears they experienced had been for their spouses. It was obvious that while Pam had made progress, she still had a long way to go to get back to the honeymoon stage.

Bob was about to speak as Cindy joined them. "I feel like I've been run over by a Mack truck," he said. "I thought I was making some progress but it's clear that I've hardly started on the road to recovery. It's all very depressing, not to mention scary. It's obvious that I must take some extended time off immediately, as Dr. Morgan suggested. The problem is how to do it. How can I take off extended time right now during our busy season when we are so short on staff?"

Bob got very emotional, which was quite unusual for him, and Sue thought she saw tears in his eyes. She felt the pain and fear with him, and thought he was going to break down and cry right there in the group. He didn't, but no one spoke for several minutes.

Finally, Cindy broke the silence. "Bob, you've made some great progress over this last month. You are at the stage where you can really benefit because you not only sense the serious nature of your problem, but you also know the solutions. It will be a roller coaster of emotions for you in the next few weeks but you are well on your way. Take courage. We are all here to help. By the way, it is okay to have a good cry from time to time, even for a man. You may need to have one soon. A good cry can clean out a lot of old baggage and clear the air for future growth."

As Cindy stood up to leave the group, she gave Bob an understanding and encouraging touch on the shoulder. Then Sue spoke to Bob. "You're right in planning to take some extended time off, but maybe for the next few weeks you simply need to cut back to halftime until you're comfortable with staffing, and the work slows down a bit. Focus only on what you have to do and spare yourself a little. Maybe I can work a bit more and cover for you. Does that sound possible?"

"It may be," Bob replied. "I definitely have to deal with my health and make some needed adjustments. I'm open to any suggestions."

"With that attitude, Bob," said Dale, "you're well on your way to finding a solution."

The four discussed a number of practical possibilities for both Pam and Bob, and by the time Cindy called the class back together it was obvious this group would support each other long after the seminar was over.

Cindy now moved into her final lecture, saying, "We must now consider our individual master plan of action for lasting change. You are familiar with our *Start, Stop, Keep* plan for improving the recipe for a better stress soup. Before doing this exercise for the final time, let's take a little time and talk about change, with some guidelines on how to do it successfully.

"There are at least three steps in making productive, long-term, positive change," Cindy continued.

"Step one is **deciding where to start with personal change**. To do this you must begin by placing a priority on those aspects of your lifestyle you need to change. Begin by looking at each change you are considering and list all the benefits and concerns you perceive. Examine carefully your expected return on the investment of time and effort. If you were investing money in the financial markets, you would want to know the return on investment to see if it was a good risk. So also as you consider making potential lifestyle changes, you need to choose areas where you are going to get the best wellness return. Three guaranteed high-wellness-return areas for physical health are quitting smoking, becoming physically active, and losing excessive weight.

"Once you have established which lifestyle changes have priority, and have focused for the best returns, you also need to target some quick-success areas where you hope to experience rapid, positive results that will encourage you to continue—areas where you can see success quickly. Some of you already did this early in this seminar by using relaxation, humour, or physical activity, and already have a number of successful changes to your credit. These quick successes will encourage you to stay with your program.

"Step two is **gaining support for your changes**. This is where you look for partners and supporters who will understand you and encourage your changes and provide accountability. In addition, take advantage of these *Eight Keys to Success*." The class followed on the overhead:

8 Keys to Success

1. Be positive.
2. Talk about your plan.
3. Socialize with role models.
4. Develop a fall-back plan.
5. Divide the change into small steps.
6. Make daily and weekly goal lists.
7. Expect setbacks.
8. Enjoy the new you.

As Cindy finished her remarks about the keys for success, she said, "Always remember to keep your sense of humour." Then she placed a slide on the overhead and said, "You may enjoy these answers that kids put on their science exam:

- A vibration is a motion that cannot make up its mind which way it wants to go.

- Vacuums are nothings. We only mention them to let them know we know they're there.

- Water vapour gets together in a cloud. When it is big enough to be called a drop, it does.

- The word trousers is an uncommon noun because it is singular at the top and plural at the bottom.

Everyone had a good laugh. Cindy seemed to have a way of introducing some humour at just the right time and often when it was least expected. Everyone was relaxed and ready for step three.

"Finally, step three, the tough one. **Decide on an effective personalized action plan that will work for you long-term**. This is where the rubber hits the road. Proper action here means success. A good plan must be **S.M.A.R.T.** To be smart it must be:

- **Specific**
- **Measurable**
- **Agreed Upon**
- **Rewarding**
- **Trackable**

"A simple example would be deciding to eat more raw fruits and vegetables. The specific goal could be to eat at least one raw fruit or vegetable at each meal. You can easily devise a simple measuring device to check on your progress. You must, of course, personally make the decision and agree upon the plan. This can be rewarding because you are now taking an effective and specific action to help prevent cancer and heart disease. Also, this is an excellent opportunity to try all those exotic fruits you haven't tasted. A simple chart can serve as a way to track your progress until the habit becomes so much a part of your life that it's automatic.

"You've been making decisions each week as we've concluded our sessions. Now is the time to make some long-term decisions and develop a long-term plan for success. Ask, *How am I going to improve my recipe for a better stress soup in the future?* Not only can you cool off the soup, but you now have all the basic tools to actually prepare and make a better life soup. Please turn to the decision page in this section and think well beyond this week and into the weeks and months ahead."

The class saw the familiar page on the screen, but with some changes. "Beside each of the three goals, this time I want you to make sure you have a smart plan for each one. Like this," instructed Cindy. The following appeared on screen as a sample of what to do:

My Action Plan For This Week

- **START:**   Regular Physical Exercise

- **Specific**   Cycling 3 days a week and walking 2 days
- **Measurable**   I will keep weekly records of progress
- **Agreed Upon**   This is my own decision
- **Rewarding**   I enjoy cycling, walking and the benefits
- **Trackable**   I will do monthly comparison charts

"Now turn to the next page in your workbook and do a SMART plan for each of your *Start, Stop, Keep* choices tonight." The group quickly found the page and went to work.

Improving The Recipe For A Better Soup

- **START:** _____

- **Specific**   _____
- **Measurable**   _____
- **Agreed Upon**   _____
- **Rewarding**   _____
- **Trackable**   _____

- **STOP:** _____

- **Specific**   _____
- **Measurable**   _____
- **Agreed Upon**   _____
- **Rewarding**   _____
- **Trackable**   _____

- KEEP: _____

- Specific _____
- Measurable _____
- Agreed Upon _____
- Rewarding _____
- Trackable _____

As the others in his group went to work, Bob decided this was too much for him right now and went outside for some air. Cindy allowed several minutes for this project. Bob returned just as she called the class back for the seminar wrap-up.

"We've already used up all our group time so I'm going to let you deal with the final plan by yourself. If you have any questions or need additional help, see me after the seminar.

"There's so much more we could share with you about managing your stress effectively. Our time is up, not only for tonight but for the seminar. You have the basics and I wish you the best as you go forward and continue to discover and implement ways to manage your stress more effectively. Remember, don't eat the soup as hot as they cook it!"

As Cindy finished speaking, the room broke out in appreciative applause with a full standing ovation. Cindy was gracious and acknowledged their gratitude. Her primary reward was knowing that the information she had shared and the support she had given was already helping many people and could save the lives of others.

The room did not empty quickly. Participants casually picked up their

> **PRACTICAL TIPS for Improving the Recipe for a Better Soup**
>
> - developing a personal action plan
> - setting aside time for planning
> - taking personal responsibility
> - choosing your priorities
> - reviewing your purpose
> - getting organized
> - organizing your workspace
> - creating a budget
> - asking the experts
> - throwing out the junk
> - taking control of your time
> - delegating tasks, responsibilities
> - using time-saving technology
> - not forgetting; writing it down
> - using "to-do" lists
> - doing essential tasks now
> - scheduling all tasks
> - planning for free time

graduation diplomas and mingled and talked. No one was in a hurry to leave. Everyone wanted to talk to and thank Cindy and Dr. Morgan personally. As Bob and Sue left with Dale and Pam, Sue remarked, "I'm glad that our neighbour Cindy lives just down the road and we can thank her personally tomorrow on our bike ride. Are you coming with us again, Pam?"

"Wouldn't miss it for the world," Pam replied. "In addition to exercise, we should make some plans for keeping in touch."

"Right," said Sue, recognizing that these friendships were a major unexpected bonus of this seminar.

The ride home was quiet for Bob and Sue. Both were in their own worlds of thought. However, later they talked well into the night and Bob had his first cleansing cry. He went to sleep feeling uncertain but hopeful of the future. He was more relaxed and peaceful, even in the midst of uncertainty, than he had been in years.

As Sue drifted off to sleep, she pondered the progress of her family in the last two months and was amazed. *We still have a long way to go to optimum wellness, but we're on our way*, she thought. *We now have the basics and will no longer eat the soup as hot as they cook it!*

Stress Management Principles

- Pinpoint and recognize the main stress producers in your life and take appropriate action—now!

- Develop an awareness of how stress is affecting you and listen to your body's stress-warning signals.

- Learn to control the stress response by calling a time out, breathing deeply, analyzing the situation, looking for humour and cutting yourself some slack.

- Learn the relaxation response and activate it often.

- Get regular daily physical activity.

- Humour is a wonderful stress buffer. Begin immediately to create a humour survival kit and use it regularly.

- Eat a wide variety of natural, plant-based foods (including some raw) for maximum energy and endurance.

- Avoid addictive drugs and resolve deep-seated stressors, such as low self-worth, grief, guilt, negative emotions, negative attitudes, unnatural anxiety and hopelessness.

- Develop an attitude of gratitude. Be thankful. Cultivate and enjoy your spirituality. Trust and nurture a personal relationship with God.

- Live life at a leisurely pace and get adequate rest. Consciously and deliberately choose joy.

- To avoid burnout, take control of your health, thoughts, behaviours, time, work, relationships, values and future, and consistently practice the 8 ways to cool off the stress soup!

- Develop a SMART plan that works for you. Make it specific, measurable, agreed upon, rewarding and trackable. Review the plan and evaluate your progress regularly.

Epilogue

I**T'S** one year later, almost to the day, since Bob and Sue Picco attended the wellness seminar and began the exciting journey to a full and balanced life.

Bob's made tremendous progress and is well on his way to a complete recovery from burnout. Regular physical activity, relaxation, good nutrition, adequate rest and balanced living have become a way of life for Bob. He has his work and family life so in balance that he's become more involved in the local Chamber of Commerce, and has been elected president for the coming year.

The banquet room is full as the annual Chamber of Commerce banquet begins. It's one of the first chamber events for Bob as president and he's invited Cindy to come and speak to all the business leaders about "Wellness in the Workplace."

When the time comes to introduce the speaker, Bob leaves his seat at the head table and walks purposefully to the microphone.

"Ladies and gentlemen," he begins. "It brings me great pleasure to introduce our speaker tonight. Over the past year Cindy Armstrong has had a powerful and very beneficial influence on me and my family. I knew from the time I was elected president, that I had to invite her to come and speak about wellness.

"Let me take a minute and share with you a bit of my wellness journey over the past year. At a very crucial time in our lives, Sue and I decided to attend a wellness seminar. That is, I agreed to go under pressure from Sue and our family physician. Had we not made serious lifestyle changes, I may have not survived the year. I was experiencing a number of serious medical symptoms and a degree of job burnout caused by overwork and poor lifestyle habits. My doctor told me right after Gary, my sales manager, dropped dead of a heart attack, that I was a heart attack looking for a place to happen! Looking back I can see how right he was!

"Improvements I have made during the past year include giving up smoking, which was a major battle for me and has been possible only with the help of Cindy and Sue. I now get regular physical exercise at least four or five times a week, and my food choices are made very carefully from food as natural as possible. I have also learned how to manage my stress much better and take regular times for relaxation and play.

"Cindy," Bob says, looking directly to her, "I've recovered to about stage two or three of burnout, and for those of you not familiar with the stages of burnout, it means that I am doing great as compared to only one year ago. I can hardly believe my improved energy levels and the joy and peace in my life compared to just twelve months ago. I am mentally more alert and physically more fit than I have been in years, and yes, even spiritually I have made some progress.

"Wellness is living life in positive balance. I haven't felt this good since I was a teenager. I recommend a wellness lifestyle to you all. In fact, some of you may wish to talk to Cindy about developing an employee wellness program for your staff. We are just beginning to do this and our employees are very excited about it."

After his short wellness testimony, Bob introduces Cindy and she gives a powerful talk on work site wellness and its importance to the business bottom line.

Sue enjoys the evening immensely, especially Bob's remarks. She is overjoyed at the progress her family's made in such a short time. *A wellness lifestyle has come to stay in the Picco home*, she muses, *and we'll be forever grateful to Cindy and Dr. Morgan for showing us the path to wellness. We know why we don't eat the soup as hot as they cook it!*

About The Author

*U*PON graduating from Loma Linda University with an Master of Science in Public Health in the area of Health Education and Promotion, and from Andrews University with an Master of Divinity, Cameron Johnston began speaking and consulting in a number of wellness areas, including smoking cessation, nutrition, fitness, stress, and weight management. After twenty years as a successful pastor and part-time health educator, Cameron became a full-time professional speaker and lifestyle consultant in 1995 and has developed a solid track record in assisting individuals, community organizations and businesses as they focus upon wellness priorities for optimum living.

Certified with the *American Seminar Leaders Association*, Cameron conducts wellness and stress management seminars and workshops throughout North America. The author of numerous articles for professional and business journals, Cameron is interviewed regularly on radio and television talk shows, including CBC Radio and CBC Television. If you are interested in receiving a free InfoPac on employee wellness or wellness seminars, please contact him at:

WellChoices™ Consulting
P.O. Box 2398, Stn. R, Kelowna, BC V1X 6A5
Phone: 1 (888) 973•3388
E-mail: cameronj@wellchoices.com
or visit our website at: www.wellchoices.com

Stress Management Seminars/Keynotes

Don't Eat The Soup As Hot As They Cook It!™

BRING our powerful, compelling, effective and fun seminar or keynote to your next convention, annual meeting or training event. Help your staff master these valuable wellness skills that could save their lives!

- Discover eight powerful stress management tools
- Assess current stress and coping levels
- Identify and eliminate harmful stress
- Determine priorities and avoid burnout
- Recognize and resolve deep-seated stress
- Maximize energy and endurance
- Increase performance and productivity
- Feel more relaxed, peaceful and confident

1000s have already benefited!

Business leaders, teachers, health care workers and clergy are saying:

"I gained more practical help in this 3-hour seminar than in a recent 2-day, stress management workshop."
— T. Fagrie, RCMP, Regina, SK

"Great seminar for executives in demanding positions."
— J. Brown, Manager, Toys "R" Us , Kamloops, BC

"The strategies for coping with stress are phenomenal. All teachers, administrators, school board and school district staff would benefit from participating in this session."
—J. Kentel, Teacher, BC School District No. 23

"This is critical information that should be available at all PD days."
— R. McEackez, 150 Mile House Elementary, BC

"Cameron recently presented two workshops on managing stress and there was 97% satisfaction with the overall program."
— P. Kenmy, Director Education Services, Atlantic Health Sciences Corporation, Saint John, NB

"This seminar has been another positive turning point in my life."
— Lieutenant D. Grice, Salvation Army Officer

Stress Management Seminars/Keynotes

The Wellness Factor

How to add 20 years to your life and enjoy every minute!

WELLNESS is an active process of making lifestyle choices for optimal well-being. It is constant personal renewal and growth as a whole person: physically, intellectually, emotionally, socially, spiritually and professionally. Here are 7 immediate benefits of sponsoring this seminar or keynote for your staff:

- Assess your current personal wellness level
- Discover and avoid 8 major health risks of today's culture
- Break free of unhealthy and dangerous culture traps
- Reduce life-threatening, health-risk factors
- Increase the potential for a long, active and enjoyable life
- Pinpoint five dynamic steps to a healthier more energetic you
- Design a strategic and effective personal wellness action plan

Participants are saying:

"This seminar was instrumental in assisting staff adopt a healthy lifestyle, it was motivating and enjoyable, and it was presented by a very relaxed facilitator. Reaction from participants was positive and indicated their expectations were met."
— J. Hawkins, RN, Education Coordinator, Dr. Hugh Twomey Health Care Centre, Botwood, NF

"Mr. Johnston is an excellent speaker. The seminar is jam-packed with wellness information covering a broad range of material and presented in a fashion that is easy to understand."
— L. Ramstead, Personnel/Administrative Assistant, BC School District No. 60, Fort St. John , BC

"It is my pleasure to recommend Cameron as a keynote speaker. His handling of wellness issues was motivating, practical and enjoyable."
— F. Finley, Principal, Northern Lights College, Fort St. John, BC

Stress Management Resources

Our powerful and compelling stress management seminar, *Don't Eat The Soup As Hot As They Cook It!* ™ is also available in the following formats:

- **3 Video Tape Set**: The complete seminar and 40-page workbook, with permission to photocopy the workbook for staff. (Over 2 hours viewing time) $295.00

- **6 Audio Tape Set**: The complete seminar and 40-page workbook. (5 hours of listening time) $95.00

Computerized Stress Assessment

THE *Computerized Stress Assessment* is a comprehensive, personalized stress management profile and effective personal wellness tool. It is designed to help people determine how well they are coping with different types of stress and to pinpoint specific problem areas. Participants complete an 8-page, easy-to-understand questionnaire which is scored by computer. A 7-page personalized report is generated which provides scores for each of three major assessment areas: Work-site Stressors, Personal Stressors, and Individual Coping Skills. Explanations and personal recommendations for improvement are given for each area. Here are the immediate benefits for you and your employees:

1. Assess accurately how well you are coping with stress
2. Pinpoint sources of work-site and personal stress
3. Uncover hidden personal stressors
4. Learn how to eliminate or modify harmful stressors
5. Strengthen self-esteem for effective stress management
6. Explore how to manage the seven key work-site stressors
7. Discover 15 ways of managing stress effectively
8. Compare current coping resources with stress levels
9. Focus on key secrets of increasing coping reserves
10. Receive personalized report with personal recommendations
11. Clarify work and family roles to reduce negative stress

Cost per individual: $49.95

The *Computerized Stress Assessment* can be combined with one-on-one stress management consulting. Please check with us for further details and pricing.

Coming Soon

Don't Eat The "TEEN" Stress Soup As Hot As They Cook It!

The Story of Derisa, a High School Student
Who Learns How to Manage Today's 24/7 Stress!

DELIGHT JOHNSTON wrote this book during her freshman year at university. In her senior year of high school, Delight served as Student Association President and learned, first-hand, the challenges of leadership. With a flair for storytelling, Delight weaves a practical but compelling account of teen life that will connect with and inspire teens as they struggle with stress in their own lives. She is currently in her senior year as a nursing student at Southern Adventist University.

Softcover, Cdn.$15.95
Available Spring 2002

Other seminars available from WellChoices™ Consulting

- Time Management
- Personal Effectiveness Strategies
- Living Life in Double Overtime (Advanced Stress Management)
- High Achievement Goal Setting
- TechnoStress: Coping with Technology
- Developing Positive Self-Esteem
- Communication Skills
- Humour in the Workplace

For further information on these seminars
and stress management resources, please contact:

WellChoices™ Consulting
P.O. Box 2398, Stn. R, Kelowna, BC v1x 6a5
Phone: 1 (888) 973•3388
E-mail: cameronj@wellchoices.com
or visit our website at: www.wellchoices.com